A SE

C000057184

W...HIPS

SELECTA

First published in England 1993 by
Wordsworth Editions Ltd
Cumberland House
Crib Street
Ware
Hertfordshire SG12 9ET

ISBN 1 85326 992 1

Photographs by courtesy of TRH Pictures London

Right: the mighty Iowa in 1940,
and 50 years later placed in reserve

Set in 8½/9pt Monophoto Univers
Text conversion and Pagination by
August Filmsetting, St Helens

Printed in Italy by Amadeus s.p.a.

Contents

Frigates

Notes about the text

Complements are identified as follows: the first figure represents the ships' officers; the second represents other ratings; the third and, where applicable the fourth, represent the air wing complement.

The number of ships in any class is identified first by the number ordered, then the number still to be commissioned, followed by the country where this is different to the country of origin, or where vessels have been ordered by more than one country, followed by the first of the class, followed by the size of the fleet. Where a class is too numerous to identify each vessel, only the first is named.

Abbreviations

CODAG   COmbined Diesel And Gas turbine
CODOG   COmbined Diesel Or Gas turbine
COGAG   COmbined Gas And Gas turbine
COGOG   COmbined Gas Or Gas turbine
COSAG   COmbined Steam and Gas turbine
EHI   European Helicopter Industries

Introduction

As we draw towards the end of the twentieth century, we find the navies of the world in a state of flux. Inflation in recent years has meant considerable reduction in construction programmes at a time when theoretical developments, combined with such practical experiences as the Falklands campaign (now already ten years ago) persuade maritime powers of the vital contribution that can be made by effective navies.

The result has been a decisive switch to a programme of rebuilding and refitting that is well underway and which will run for some years yet.

Technological advances in the field of sensors and weaponry have outstripped original construction programmes for new ships, and thus they are as easy to incorporate into a refit. Meanwhile, the new vessels are built to a more flexible configuration with the major powers' single-role ships needing to possess secondary, if not multi-role, capabilities.

Owing to limited space, we have been forced to make selections for inclusion but have endeavoured to include as large a variety as possible, depicting the evolution of the major warships over the past half-century.

Ship designations

Aircraft carriers

CV	multi-role
CVLS	light, anti-submarine
CVG	guided missile
CVGN	nuclear powered, guided missile
CVL	light
CVHS	helicopter, anti-submarine
CVN	nuclear powered

Battleships

BB

Battle cruisers

CBGN   nuclear powered guided missile

Cruisers

CG	guided missile
CGN	nuclear powered guided missile
CA	gun

Destroyers

DDG	guided missile
DD	gun

Frigates

FFG   guided missile

Charles de Gaulle class

Type: nuclear-powered multi-role aircraft carrier
Country of origin: France
Displacement: 34,000 tons normal and 36,000 tons full load
Dimensions: length 261.5m (857.7ft); beam 31.8m (104.3ft); draught 8.5m (27.8ft); flight deck length 261.5m (857.7ft) and width 62m (203.4ft)
Gun armament: none
Aircraft: 40 fixed-wing, plus rotary-wing
Electronics: surveillance radar, air search radar, air/surface search radar, fire-control radar, navigation radar, landing radar, satellite navigation system and torpedo-warning sonar
Propulsion: two Type K15 pressurised water-cooled reactors supplying steam to two sets of geared turbines delivering 61,150kW (82,015 shp) to two shafts
Performance: maximum speed 27kt
Complement: 1,150 plus and air group of 550
Ships: two, *Charles de Gaulle* and *Richelieu*

Laid down in 1989, the Charles de Gaulle *is due to be commissioned in 1996*

Clemenceau class

Type: multi-role aircraft carrier
Country of origin: France
Displacement: 27,310 tons normal and 32,780 tons full load
Dimensions: length 265m (869.4ft); beam 31.72m (104.1ft); draught 8.6m (28.2ft); flight deck length 257m (843.2ft) width 29.5m (96.8ft)
Gun armament: eight 100mm (3.9in) L/55 DP
Aircraft: 40 fixed-wing (20 Dassault-Breguet Super Etendards, 10 Vought F-8 Crusaders and 10 Dassault-Breguet Alizés) and four rotary-wing (two Super Frelons and two Alouette IIIs)
Electronics: Thomson-CSF DRBV 20 surveillance radar; Thomson-CSF DRBC 20C air-warning radar; Thomson-CSF DRBI 10 height-finding radars, Thomson-CSF DRBC 32 fire-control radars, Decca 1226 navigation radar, NRBA landing radar, SQS-503 sonar, SENIT 2 combat information system and electronic countermeasures
Propulsion: six boilers supplying steam to two sets of Parsons geared turbines delivering 93,960kW (126,000shp) to two shafts
Performance: maximum speed 32kt; range 13,900km (8,635 miles) at 18kt or 6,500km (4,040 miles) at 32kt
Complement: 64 + 476 + 798
Ships: two, *Clemenceau* and *Foch*

The first aircraft carriers designed by the French

Enterprise class

Type: nuclear-powered multi-role aircraft carrier
Country of origin: USA
Displacement: 75,700 tons standard and 89,000 tons full load
Dimensions: length 335.9m (1,102ft); beam 40.5m (133ft); draught 10.9m (35.8ft); flight deck width 76.8m (252ft)
Gun armament: three Phalanx Mk 15 20mm (0.79in) close-in weapon systems, and three 20mm (0.79in) Mk 68 mountings
Missile armament: three Mk 57 launchers for RIM-7 NATO Sea Sparrow
Aircraft: about 84
Electronics: surface and air search radar, aircraft landing radar, missile fire control and technical data systems, satellite antenna, and chaff systems
Propulsion: eight pressurised water-cooled Westinghouse A2W reactors supplying steam to four sets of Westinghouse geared turbines delivering 208,795kW (280,000shp) to four shafts
Performance: maximum speed 35kt; range 741,245km (460,600 miles)
Complement: 162 + 2,940, and a carrier airwing complement of 304 + 2,323
Ships: one, *Enterprise*

The Enterprise **was the world's first**
14 **nuclear-powered aircraft carrier**

Forrestal class

Type: multi-role aircraft carrier
Country of origin: USA
Displacement: 56,060 tons standard and 75,900 tons full load
Dimensions: length 331m (1,086ft); beam 39.5m (129.5ft); draught 11.3m (37ft); flight deck width 76.8m (252ft)
Gun armament: to be fitted with three 20mm (0.79in) Phalanx Mk 16
Missile armament: two Mk 25 octuple launchers for RIM-7 Sea Sparrow SAMS
Aircraft: about 70
Electronics: Westinghouse low-angled air-search radar, Raytheon/Sylvania surface-search radar, air-search radar, navigation radar, missile fire-control systems, Naval Tactical Data System, satellite communications antenna and Mk 36 Super Chaff launchers
Propulsion: eight Babcock & Wilcox boilers supplying steam to four sets of Westinghouse geared turbines delivering 193,880kW (260,000 shp)
Performance: maximum speed 33kt; range 14,805km (9,200 miles) at 20kt or 7,400km (4,600 miles) at 30kt
Complement: 145 + 2,645, and a carrier air-wing complement of about 2,150
Ships: four; *Forrestal, Saratoga, Ranger* and *Independence*

Garibaldi class

Type: light anti-submarine aircraft carrier
Country of origin: Italy
Displacement: 10,100 tons standard and 13,370 tons full load
Dimensions: length 180m (590.4ft); beam 30.4m (99.7ft); draught 6.7m (22ft); flight deck length 174m (570.7ft), width 30.4m (99.7ft)
Gun armament: six 40mm (1.58in) Breda L/70 AA in three twin mountings
Missile armament: two Twin Teseo launchers for 10 Otomat Mk 2 surface-to-surface missiles, and two Albatros launchers for Aspide surface-to-air missiles
Anti-submarine armament: two triple ILAS 3 tube mountings for 324mm (12.75in) A244S or 324mm (12.75in) Mk 46 A6S torpedoes, and helicopter-launched weapons
Aircraft: up to 18 Agusta-Sikorsky SH-3 Sea King helicopters
Propulsion: four General Electric-Fiat LM2500 gas turbines delivering 59,655kW (80,000shp) to two shafts
Performance: maximum speed 30kt; range 13,000km (8,080 miles) at 20kt
Complement: 550 (accommodation is available for 825)
Ships: one, *Guiseppe Garibaldi*

Hermes class

Type: multi-role aircraft carrier
Country of origin: UK/India
Displacement: 23,900 tons standard and 28,700 tons full load
Dimensions: length 226.9m (744.3ft); beam 27.4m (90ft); draught 8.7m (28.5ft); flight deck length 226.9m (744.3ft) and width 48.8m (160ft)
Gun armament: none
Missile armament: Soviet SAM system to be fitted
Torpedo armament: none
Anti-submarine armament: helicopter-launched weapons
Aircraft: maximum 37 aircraft, usually six STOVL fighters and seven helicopters
Electronics: air-search, air/surface-search, navigation radars and fire-control systems
Propulsion: four Admiralty boilers supplying steam to two sets of Parsons geared turbines delivering 56,675kW (76,000shp) to two shafts
Performance: maximum speed 28kt
Complement: 143 + 1,207 including air group
Ships: one, *Viraat*

HMS Hermes, **renamed** Viraat, **with the**
Indian Navy

Invincible class

Type: light multi-role aircraft carrier
Country of origin: UK
Displacement: 16,256 tons standard and 20,000 tons full load
Dimensions: length 206.6m (677ft); beam 27.5m (90ft); draught 7.3m (24ft); flight deck length 167.8m (550ft) and width 31.9m (105ft)
Gun armament: two 20mm (0.79in) Phalanx CIWS mountings and two 20mm (0.79in) AA
Missile armament: one twin launcher for 22 Sea Dart surface-to-air missiles
Anti-submarine armament: helicopter-launched weapons
Aircraft: 10 BAe Sea Harrier FRS. Mk1V/STOL aircraft and nine Westland Sea King HAS.Mk 2/5 helicopters
Propulsion: four Rolls-Royce Olympus TM3B gas turbines delivering 83,520kW (112,000shp) to two shafts
Performance: maximum speed 28kt; range 9,250km (5,750 miles) at 15kt
Complement: 131 + 131 + 869 + 284 air group personnel
Ships: three; *Invincible*, *Illustrious* and *Ark Royal*

Refits in 1988 added accommodation for a further 120 crew

John F Kennedy class

Type: multi-role aircraft carrier
Country of origin: USA
Displacement: 61,000 tons standard and 82,000 tons full load
Dimensions: length 320.7m (1,052ft); beam 39.6m (130ft); draught 10.9m (35.9ft); flight deck width 76.9m (252ft)
Gun armament: three 20mm (0.79in) Phalanx Mk 15 close-in weapon system mountings
Missile armament: three Mk 29 launchers for RIM-7 Sea Sparrow surface-to-air missiles
Aircraft: about 85
Electronics: surface-search radar, air-search radar, navigation radar, landing radars, missile fire-control systems, Naval Tactical Data System, several advanced electronic warfare systems, satellite communications antenna and rapid-blooming overhead chaff launchers
Propulsion: eight Foster-Wheeler boilers supplying steam to four sets of Westinghouse geared turbines delivering 208,795kW (280,000 shp) to four shafts
Performance: Maximum speed 30+ kt; range 14,805km (9,200 miles) at 20kt
Complement: 150+2,645, and a carrier air wing complement of about 2,150
Ships: one, *John F Kennedy*

John F Kennedy **is closely related to**
24   **the Kitty Hawk class**

Kiev (Modified) class

Type: multi-role hybrid aircraft carrier
Country of origin: USSR
Displacement: 30,000 tons standard and 37,000 tons full load
Dimensions: length 273m (895.7ft); beam 32.7m (107.3ft); width 47.2m (154.8ft); draught 10m (32.8ft); flight deck length 189m (620ft) and width 20.7m (68ft)
Gun armament: two 100mm (3.93in) L/70 DP in single mountings and eight 30mm (1.18in) ADGM 630 CIWS mountings
Missile armament: six twin container-launchers for 28 SS-N-12 'Sandbox' anti-ship missiles and four groups of six octuple vertical launchers for 192 SA-N-9 SAMs
Aircraft: 13 fixed-wing and 19 rotary-wing
Electronics: surveillance, air-search, surface search, fire-control, aircraft control and navigation radars
Propulsion: eight boilers supplying steam to four sets of geared turbines delivering 150,000kW (201,180shp) to four shafts
Performance: maximum speed 32kt; range 24,100km (14,975 miles) at 18kt
Complement: 1,200 excluding air group
Ships: one, *Baku*

Baku **carries considerably improved electronics and armaments over the original Kiev class**

Kitty Hawk class

Type: multi-role aircraft carrier
Country of origin: USA
Displacement: *Kitty Hawk* 60,100 tons standard and 80,000 tons full load
Dimensions: *Kitty Hawk* length 318.8m (1,064ft); beam 39.6m (130ft); draught 11.3m (37ft); flight deck width 76.9m (252ft)
Gun armament: three 20mm (0.79in) Phalanx Mk 15
Missile armament: three Mk 29 octuple launchers for 24 RIM-7 Sea Sparrow SAMs
Anti-submarine armament: air-dropped weapons
Aircraft: about 85
Electronics: air-search radar, height-finding radar, navigation radar, missile fire-control systems, Naval Tactical Data System, advanced electronic warfare systems, satellite communications antenna and Super Chaffroc
Propulsion: eight Foster-Wheeler boilers supplying steam to four sets of Westinghouse geared turbines delivering 208,795kW (208,000shp) to four shafts
Performance: maximum speed 30+ kt; range 14,805km (9,200 miles) at 20kt or 7,400km (4,600 miles) at 30kt
Complement: 150+2,645+2,150 air wing
Ships: three; *Kitty Hawk*, *Constellation* and *America*

Midway class

Type: multi-role aircraft carrier
Country of origin: USA
Displacement: 51,000 tons standard and 62,200 tons full load for CV41, or 52,000 tons standard and 62,200 tons full load for CV43
Dimensions: length 298.4m (979ft); beam 36.9m (121ft); draught 10.8m (35.3ft); flight deck width 72.5m (238ft)
Gun armament: three 20mm (0.79in) Phalanx Mk 15 close-in weapon system mountings
Missile armament: two Mk 25 launchers for RIM-7 Sea Sparrow surface-to-air missiles
Aircraft: about 75
Armour: multi-layer protection afforded by thin armour on several decks
Electronics: 3D radar, combined air and surface-search radar, air-search radar, navigation radar, carrier-controlled approach radar, Naval Tactical Data System, satellite communications antenna and Super Chaffroc rapid-blooming overhead chaff launchers
Propulsion: 12 Babcock & Wilcox boilers supplying steam to four sets of Westinghouse geared turbines delivering 158,090kW (212,000shp) to four shafts
Performance: maximum speed 30+ kt
Complement: 140+2,475 and an air wing strength of about 1,800
Ships: two, *Midway* and *Coral Sea*

Moskva class

Type: anti-submarine helicopter carrier
Country of origin: USSR
Displacement: 14,000 tons standard and 17,500 tons full load
Dimensions: length 190.5m (624ft); beam 23m (75.4ft); draught 11m (36.1ft); flight deck length 81m (265.7ft)
Gun armament: four 57mm (2.25in) L/70 AA
Missile armament: two twin launchers for 48 SA-N-3 and 'Goblet' surface-to-air missiles
Anti-submarine armament: one twin SUW-N-1 launcher for 20 FRAS-1 missiles, two RBU 6000 12-barrel rocket launchers and helicopter-launched weapons
Aircraft: 14 Kamov Ka-25 'Hormone-A'
Electronics: one 'Top Sail' 3D radar, one 'Head Net-C' 3D radar, two 'Head Light' SAM-control radars, two 'Muff Cob' AA gun-control radars and three 'Don-2' navigation radars
Propulsion: four boilers supplying steam to two sets of geared turbines delivering 74,570kW (100,000shp) to two shafts
Performance: maximum speed 30kt; range 16,675km (10,360 miles) at 18kt or 5,200km (3,230 miles) at 30kt
Complement: 840 excluding air group
Ships: two, *Moskva* and *Leningrad*

Both ships have a large helicopter deck aft, and all armament forward of the superstructure

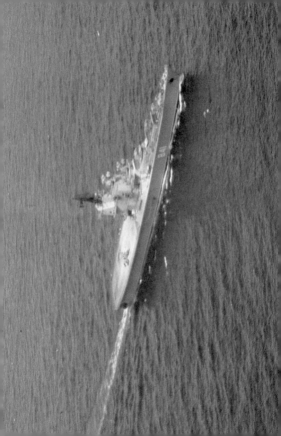

Nimitz class

Type: nuclear-powered multi-role aircraft carrier
Country of origin: USA
Displacement: 72,700 tons light, 81,600 tons standard and 91,485 tons full load (CVNs 68-70) or 96,350 tons full load (CVNs 71-73)
Dimensions: length 332.9m (1,092ft); beam 40.8m (134ft); draught 11.3m (37ft); flight deck width 76.8m (252ft)
Gun armament: two 20mm (0.79in) Phalanx Mk 15 close-in weapon-system mountings
Missile armament: three Mk 29 launchers for 24 RIM-7 Sea Sparrow surface-to-air missiles
Aircraft: 85-90
Propulsion: two pressurised water cooled nuclear reactors (Westinghouse A4W or General Electric A1G) supplying steam to four sets of geared turbines delivering 193,880kW (260,000 shp) to four shafts
Performance: maximum speed 30+ kt
Complement: 3,300 and a carrier air wing strength of 2,800
Ships: eight; *Nimitz, Dwight D Eisenhower, Carl Vinson, Theodore Roosevelt, Abraham Lincoln* and *George Washington,* + two

With two ships recently laid down, the Nimitz class carriers will continue well into the twenty-first
century

Iowa class

Type: battleship
Country of origin: USA
Displacement: 45,000 tons standard and 58,000 tons full load
Dimensions: length 270.4m (887.2ft); beam 33m (108.2ft); draught 11.6m (38ft)
Gun armament: nine 406.5mm (16in), 12 127 mm (5in) and four 20mm (0.79in) mountings
Missile armament: 32 Tomahawk land attack and anti-ship cruise missiles and 16 Harpoon anti-ship missiles
Aircraft: provision for 3/4 helicopters on aft platform
Electronics: long-range air-search, medium-range air/surface search and navigation radars; gun directors controlled by fire-control system; warning and jamming systems, chaff/flare launchers, torpedo-decoy system and satellite communications system
Propulsion: eight Babcock & Wilcox boilers supplying steam to four sets of geared turbines delivering 158,090kW (212,000shp) to four shafts
Performance: maximum speed 33kt; range 27,800km (17,275 miles) at 17kt
Complement: 1,571
Ships: four; *Iowa, New Jersey, Missouri* and *Wisconsin*

Recommissioned in the 1980s, forming the world's only true battleship class

Kirov class

Type: nuclear-powered guided missile battle cruiser
Country of origin: USSR
Displacement: 19,000 tons standard and 23,500 tons full load
Dimensions: length 250m (820.2ft); beam 28.5m (93.5ft); draught 10m (32.8ft)
Gun armament: two 100mm (3.9in) and eight 30mm (1.18in) mountings
Missile armament: 20 launch tubes for 20 SS-N-19, 12 launch tubes for 96 SA-N-6, and two twin launchers for SA-N-4 missiles
Torpedo armament: 533mm (21in) tube mountings
Anti-submarine armament: twin launcher for 16 SS-N-14 'Silex' anti-submarine missiles
Aircraft: three Kamov KA-25 'Hormone-A' helicopters on a platform aft
Electronics: 3D radar, control radars, main armament control radars, AA gun control radars, navigation radars, sonar and electronic counter-measures
Propulsion: two nuclear reactors with boilers supplying steam to turbines delivering 119,300kW (160,000shp)
Performance: maximum speed 35kt
Complement: 900
Ships: four; *Kirov, Frunze* and *Kalinin, +* one

These CBGÑs are exceptionally
38 *powerful and potently armed*

Andrea Doria class

Type: guided missile cruiser
Country of origin: Italy
Displacement: 5,000 tons standard and 6,500 tons full load
Dimensions: length 149.3m (489.8ft); beam 17.2m (56.4ft); draught 5m (16.4ft)
Gun armament: eight 76mm (3in) OTO Melara L/62 in single mountings
Missile armament: one twin launcher for 40 RIM-67A Standard-ER surface-to-air missiles
Anti-submarine armament: two triple Mk 32 tube mountings for 324mm (12.75in) Mk 46 A/S torpedoes and helicopter-launched torpedoes
Aircraft: four Agusta-Bell AB.212 ASW helicopters
Propulsion: four Foster-Wheeler boilers supplying steam to two double-reduction geared turbines delivering 44,740kW (60,000shp) to two shafts
Performance: maximum speed 31kt; range 9,250km (5,750 miles) at 17kt
Complement: 45 + 425
Ships: two, *Andrea Doria* and *Caio Duilio*

Caio Duilio **carries only two**
helicopters and six main guns

Bainbridge class

Type: nuclear-powered guided missile cruiser
Country of origin: USA
Displacement: 7,600 tons standard and 8,592 tons full load
Dimensions: length 172.3m (565ft); beam 17.6m (57.9ft); draught 7.7m (25.4ft)
Gun armament: two 20mm (0.79in) AA in a Mk 67 twin mounting
Missile armament: Harpoon surface-to-surface missiles and 80 Standard ER surface-to-air missiles
Anti-submarine armament: octuple ASROC launcher and tube mountings for 324mm (12.75in) torpedoes
Electronics: air-search, surface-search and fire-control radars; missile fire-control systems, weapons-direction system, Naval Tactical Data system and satellite communications antenna
Propulsion: two General Electric D2G pressurised water cooled reactors supplying steam to two geared turbines delivering 44,740kW (60,000shp) to two shafts
Performance: maximum speed 38kt
Complement: 34 + 436, and flag accommodation for 6 + 12
Ships: one, *Bainbridge*

The Bainbridge *is a nuclear-powered version of the Leahy class cruisers*

Belknap class

Type: guided missile light cruiser
Country of origin: USA
Displacement: 6,570 tons standard and 7,900 tons full load
Dimensions: length 166.7m (547ft); beam 16.7m (54.8ft); draught 8.8m (28.8ft) to bottom of sonar dome and 5.8m (19ft) to keel
Gun armament: one 127mm (5in) L/54 in a Mk 42 mounting, and two 20mm (0.79in) Phalanx Mk 15 close-in system mountings
Missile armament: two quadruple launchers for eight RGM-84A Harpoon surface-to-surface missiles; Mk 10 twin launcher for 40 RIM-67B Standard SM-2 SAMs, and (to be fitted) BGM-109 Tomahawk cruise missiles
Anti-submarine armament: two triple Mk 32 tube mountings for 324mm (12.75in) Mk 44/46 A/S torpedoes, and up to 20 RUR-5A ASROC missiles fired from the Mk 10 launcher
Aircraft: one Kaman SH-2F Seasprite
Propulsion: four Babcock & Wilcox boilers supplying steam to two sets of geared General Electric turbines delivering 63,385kW (85,000shp) to two shafts
Performance: maximum speed 32.5kt
Complement: 31 + 387 squadron staff or 520 (CG 26 including flag accommodation)
Ships: nine; *Belknap* + eight

Designed for both surface-to-air and surface-to-underwater action

California class

Type: nuclear-powered guided missile cruiser
Country of origin: USA
Displacement: 9,560 tons standard and 11,100 tons full load
Dimensions: length 181.7m (596ft); beam 18.6m (61ft); draught 9.6m (31.5ft)
Gun armament: two 127mm (5in) L/54 DP in two Mk 42 single mountings, and (to be fitted) two Phalanx Mk 15 20mm (0.79in) close-in weapons system mountings
Missile armament: eight BGM-109 Tomahawk surface-to-surface missiles, eight RGM-84A Harpoon surface-to-surface missiles and 80 RIM-66C Standard MR surface-to-air missiles
Anti-submarine armament: one octuple Mk 16 launcher for RUR-5A ASROC missiles, and two triple Mk 32 tube mountings for 324mm (12.75in) Mk 46 A/S torpedoes
Propulsion: two General Electric D2G pressurised water cooled reactors supplying steam to two geared turbines delivering 44,740kW (60,000shp) to two shafts
Performance: maximum speed 30kt; nuclear core life about 1,126,500km (700,000 miles)
Complement: 28 + 512
Ships: two, *California* and *South Carolina*

Both lack the capabilities of the Virginia class, and three ships planned were never laid down

Kara class

Type: guided missile cruiser
Country of origin: USSR
Displacement: 8,200 tons standard and 10,000 tons full load
Dimensions: length 173.2m (568ft); beam 18m (59ft); draught 6.7m (22ft)
Gun armament: four 76mm (3in) L/60 DP in two twin mountings and four 30mm (1.18in) AA 'Gatling' mountings
Missile armament: eight SS-N-14 surface-to-underwater missiles, 72 SA-N-3 'Goblet' SAMs missiles and 36 SA-N-4 'Gecko' SAMs
Torpedo armament: two quintuple 533mm (21in) AS/ASW tube mountings
Anti-submarine armament: two RBU 6,000 12-barrel and two RBU 1,000 six-barrel rocket launchers and helicopter-launched weapons
Aircraft: One Kamov KA-25 'Hormone-A'
Propulsion: COGOG arrangement, with two gas turbines delivering 17,900kW (24,000shp) and four gas turbines delivering 74,570kW (100,000shp) to two shafts
Performance: maximum speed 33kt; range 14,825km (9,210 miles) at 18kt or 3,700km (2,300 miles) at 32kt
Complement: 30 + 510
Ships: seven; *Nikolayev, Ochakov, Kerch, Azov, Petropavlovsk, Tashkent* and *Tallinn*

A big advance on the Kresta II class, built at the Nikolayev North shipyard

Kresta II class

Type: guided missile cruiser
Country of origin: USSR
Displacement: 6,400 tons standard and 7,800 tons full load
Dimensions: length 158.5m (520ft); beam 16.9m (55.45ft); draught 6m (19.7ft)
Gun armament: four 57mm (2.25in) and four 30mm (1.18in)
Missile armament: 533mm (21in) mountings for Type 53 dual-role torpedoes
Anti-submarine armament: container launchers for eight 'Silex' missiles, 12-barrel and six-barrel rocket launchers, and helicopter-launched weapons
Aircraft: one Kamov Ka-25 helicopter
Electronics: air-search, air/surface search, surface-search, navigation and fire-control radars, comprehensive surveillance measures and chaff launchers
Propulsion: four boilers supplying steam to two sets of geared turbines delivering 82,000kW (109,980shp) to two shafts
Performance: maximum speed 35kt; range 13,000km (8,080 miles) at 18kt
Complement: 400
Ships: 10; *Kronstadt* + nine

A basically well-armed anti-submarine class with improved SAM capability

Kynda class

Type: guided-missile cruiser
Country of origin: USSR
Displacement: 4,400 tons standard and 5,700 tons full load
Dimensions: length 142m (465.8ft); beam 15.8m (51.8ft); draught 5.3m (17.4ft)
Gun armament: four 76mm (3in) L/60 DP
Missile armament: 16 SS-N-3B and 22 SA-N-1 surface-to surface missiles
Torpedo armament: two triple 533mm (21in) AS/ASW tube mountings
Anti-submarine armament: two RBU 6000 12-barrel rocket launchers
Aircraft: one Kamov Ka-25 helicopter
Electronics: two 'Head Net-A' air-search radars, two 'Plinth Net' surface-search radars, two 'Scoop Pair' SSM-control radars, one 'Peel Group' SAM-control radar, two 'Owl Screech' gun-control radars and two 'Don-2' navigation radars
Propulsion: four boilers supplying steam to two sets of geared turbines delivering 74,570kW (100,000shp) to two shafts
Performance: maximum speed 34kt; range 11,125km (6,915 miles) at 15kt or 2,775km (1,725 miles) at 34kt
Complement: 390
Ships: four; *Grozny* + three

The building of the class was halted in favour of anti-submarine types

Leahy class

Type: guided missile cruiser
Country of origin: USA
Displacement: 5,670 tons standard and 7,800 tons full load
Dimensions: length 162.5m (533ft); beam 16.6m (54.9ft); draught 7.6m (24.8ft) to dome
Gun armament: two 20mm (0.79in) Phalanx Mk 15 close-in weapon system mountings
Missile armament: two quadruple container-launchers for eight RGM-84A Harpoon surface-to-surface missiles, and two Mk 10 twin launchers for 80 RIM-67B Standard-ER SAMs
Anti-submarine armament: two triple Mk 32 tube mountings for 324mm (12.75in) Mk 46 A/S torpedoes, and one octuple launcher for RUR-5A ASROC missiles
Aircraft: Provision for one Kaman SH-2F Seasprite on a platform aft
Propulsion: four Babcock & Wilcox boilers supplying steam to two sets of General Electric geared turbines delivering 63,385kW (85,000shp) to two shafts
Performance: maximum speed 32.7kt; range 14,805km (9,200 miles) at 20kt
Complement: 18 + 359 and flag accommodation for 6 + 18
Ships: nine; *Leahy* + eight

Purpose-built as an escort to aircraft carriers, their primary armament is surface-to-air missiles

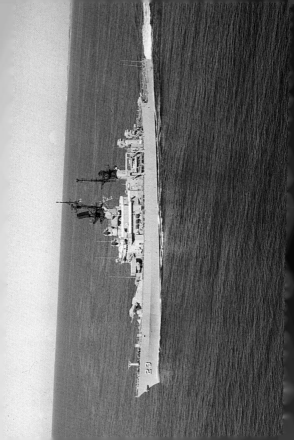

Long Beach class

Type: nuclear-powered guided missile cruiser
Country of origin: USA
Displacement: 14,200 tons standard and 17,100 tons full load
Dimensions: length 219.9m (721.1ft); beam 22.3m (73.2ft); draught 9.1m (26.7ft)
Gun armament: two 127mm (5in) L/38 DP in Mk 30 single mountings, and two 20mm (0.79in) Phalanx Mk 15 close-in weapon system mountings
Missile armament: two quadruple container-launchers for eight RGM-84A anti-ship missiles, two Mk 10 twin launchers for RIM-67B Standard-ER surface-to-air missiles
Anti-submarine armament: two triple Mk 32 tube mountings for 324mm (12.75in) Mk 46 A/S torpedoes and one octuple launcher for RUR-5A ASROC missiles
Aircraft: provision for a helicopter
Propulsion: two Westinghouse C1W pressurised water cooled reactors supplying steam to two sets of General Electric geared turbines delivering 59,655kW (80,000shp) to two shafts
Performance: maximum speed 36kt
Complement: 79 + 1,081 and flag accommodation for 10 + 58
Ships: one, *Long Beach*

The world's first nuclear-powered surface combatant, Long Beach *was*
56 *commissioned in 1961*

Ticonderoga class

Type: guided missile cruiser
Country of origin: USA
Displacement: 9,600 tons full load
Dimensions: length 172.8m (566.8ft); beam 16.8m (55ft); draught 9.5m (31ft)
Gun armament: two 127mm (5in) L/54 DP in two Mk 45 single mountings, and two 20mm (0.79in) Phalanx Mk 15
Missile armament: two octuple container-launchers for 16 RGM-84A Harpoon surface-to-surface missiles and two Mk 26 twin launchers for up to 68 RIM-67B Standard surface-to-air missiles; CG49 onwards will have two EX 41 vertical launchers for up to 122 assorted missiles, and from CG52 onwards will have two Vertical Launch Systems with 24 BGM-109 Tomahawk surface-to-surface cruise missiles
Anti-submarine armament: two triple Mk 32 tube mountings for 324mm (12.75in) Mk 46 A/S torpedoes and up to 20 RUR-5A ASROC missiles as part of the total missile strength
Aircraft: two Sikorsky SH-60B Seahawk
Propulsion: four General Electric LM 2500 gas turbines delivering 59,655kW (80,000shp) to two shafts
Performance: maximum speed 30+ kt
Complement: 33+327
Ships: 27 (5); *Ticonderoga* + 21

Three further craft will be commissioned in 1993

Truxton class

Type: nuclear powered guided missile cruiser
Country of origin: USA
Displacement: 8,200 tons standard and 9,125 tons full load
Dimensions: length 171.9m (564ft); beam 17.7m (58ft); draught 9.4m (31ft)
Gun armament: one 127mm (5in) L/54 DP and two 20mm (0.79in) Phalanx Mk 15
Missile armament: eight Harpoon surface-to-surface and 60 Standard-ER surface-to-air missiles
Anti-submarine armament: Mk 46 A/S torpedoes and up to 20 ASROC missiles
Aircraft: one Kaman SH-2F Seasprite helicopter
Electronics: 3D radar, air-search, surface-search and gun-control radar; fire-control system
Propulsion: two pressurised water cooled General Electric D2G nuclear reactors supplying steam to two sets of geared turbines delivering 44,740kW (60,000shp) to two shafts
Performance: maximum speed 38kt
Complement: 36 + 492, and flag accommodation for 6 + 12
Ships: one, *Truxtun*

Truxton **is a Belknap class disguised with a nuclear powerplant**

Virginia class

Type: nuclear-powered guided missile cruiser
Country of origin: USA
Displacement: 8,625 tons standard and 10,400 tons full load
Dimensions: length 178.4m (585ft); beam 19.2m (63ft); draught 9m (29.5ft)
Gun armament: two 127mm (5in) L/54 DP and two 20mm (0.79in) Phalanx
Missile armament: two quadruple container-launchers for eight RGM-84A Harpoon surface-to-surface missiles, two Mk 26 twin launchers for a maximum of 50 RIM-67B Standard-MR surface-to-air missiles and two quadruple launchers for eight BGM-109 Tomahawk cruise missiles
Anti-submarine armament: two triple Mk 32 tube mountings for 324mm (12.75in) Mk 46 A/S torpedoes, up to 20 RUR-5A ASROC missiles launched from the Mk 26 launchers
Aircraft: two Sikorsky SH-60 Seahawk helicopters
Propulsion: two pressurised water cooled General Electric D2G nuclear reactors supplying steam to two sets of geared turbines delivering 74,570kW (100,000shp) to two shafts
Performance: maximum speed 40kt
Complement: 27 + 445
Ships: four; *Virginia* + three

California class lookalikes with twin SAM launchers

Vittorio Veneto class

Type: guided missile cruiser
Country of origin: Italy
Displacement: 7,500 tons standard and 8,850 tons full load
Dimensions: length 179.6m (589ft); beam 19.4m (63.3ft); draught 6m (19.7ft)
Gun armament: eight 76mm (3in) L/62 DP and six 40mm (1.58in) Breda L/70 AA
Missile armament: four Otomat anti-ship missiles and 60 RIM-67A Standard SM-1 ER SAMs
Anti-submarine armament: Mk 46 torpedoes, up to 20 RUR-5A ASROC anti-ship missiles and helicopter-launched weapons
Aircraft: up to nine helicopters
Electronics: air-search, surface-search, target indication, navigation, illumination and guidance radars; fire-control systems, warning and jamming elements and chaff/flare launchers
Propulsion: four Ansaldo/Foster-Wheeler boilers supplying steam to two sets of geared turbines delivering 54,500kW (73,095shp) to two shafts
Performance: maximum speed 32kt; range 9,250km (5,750 miles) at 17kt
Complement: 50 + 500
Ships: one, *Vittorio Veneto*

Very much an enlarged version of the Andrea Doria, the Vittorio Veneto carries nine helicopters

64

Amatsukaze or Type 163 class

Type: anti-aircraft and anti-submarine guided missile destroyer
Country of origin: Japan
Displacement: 3,050 tons standard and 4,000 tons full load
Dimensions: length 131m (429.8ft); beam 13.4m (44ft); draught 4.2m (13.8ft)
Gun armament: four 76mm (3in) L/50 DP in two Mk 33 twin mountings
Missile armament: one Mk 13 single launcher for 40 RIM-66B Standard SM-1 MR SAMs
Anti-submarine armament: one Mk 16 octuple launcher for eight RUR-5A ASROC missiles, two Mk 32 triple 324mm (12.75in) mountings for Mk 46 torpedoes and two Hedgehog Mk 15 mortars
Electronics: 3D, medium-range air-search, surface-search, illumination and tracking radars, fire-control systems, warning and jamming elements and two chaff launchers
Propulsion: two Ishikawajima/Foster-Wheeler boilers supplying steam to two sets of Ishikawajima/General Electric geared turbines delivering 44,750kW (60,010shp) to two shafts
Performance: maximum speed 33kt; range 12,975km (8,065 miles) at 18kt
Complement: 290
Ships: one, *Amatsukaze*

A single-unit class commissioned in
1965

Arleigh Burke class

Type: multi-role guided missile escort destroyer
Country of origin: USA
Displacement: 8,200 tons standard and 8,500 tons full load
Dimensions: length 153.6m (504ft); beam 20.4m (66.9ft); draught 9.1m (29.6ft)
Gun armament: one 127mm (5in) L/54 DP and two 20mm (0.79in) Phalanx
Missile armament: eight RGM-84 Harpoon anti-ship missiles, 90 RUR-5A ASROC anti-submarine, RIM-66C Standard SM-2 MR surface-to-air and BGM-109 Tomahawk anti-ship and land-attack cruise missiles
Anti-submarine armament: Mk 46 or Mk 50 torpedoes and helicopter-launched weapons
Aircraft: one Sikorsky SH-60B Seahawk
Electronics: 3D phased-array air-search, surface search, fire-control systems and satellite navigation systems
Propulsion: COGAG arrangement, four General Electric LM 2500-30 gas turbines delivering 74,570kW (100,000shp) to two shafts
Performance: maximum speed 32kt; range 9,250km (5,750 miles) at 20kt
Complement: 23 + 280
Ships: four; *Arleigh Burke*, *John Barry*, *John Paul Jones* and *Curtis Wilbur*

Partner to the Ticonderoga replacing the Leahy, Belknap and Coontz

Asagiri or Type 134 class

Type: anti-submarine and anti-ship guided missile destroyer
Country of origin: Japan
Displacement: 3,500 tons standard and 4,200 tons full load
Dimensions: length 137m (449.5ft); beam 14.6m (47.9ft); draught 4.45m (14.6ft)
Gun armament: one 76mm (3in) OTO Melara L/62 DP and two 20mm (0.79in) Phalanx Mk 15
Missile armament: eight RGM-84 Harpoon anti-ship missiles and RIM-7 NATO Sea Sparrow SAMs
Torpedo armament: none
Anti-submarine armament: 16 RUR-5A ASROC missiles, Mk 46 torpedoes and helicopter-launched weapons
Aircraft: one helicopter in a hangar aft
Electronics: air-search and surface-search radars, fire-control system, warning and jamming elements and chaff/flare launchers
Propulsion: COGAG (COmbined Gas turbine And Gas turbine) arrangement, with four Rolls-Royce Spey SM1A gas turbines delivering 40,260kW (54,000shp) to two shafts
Performance: maximum speed 30+ kt
Complement: 220
Ships: seven; *Asagiri* + six

The Spey gas turbines make these seven units effective and economical

Audace class

Type: guided missile destroyer
Country of origin: Italy
Displacement: 3,950 tons standard and 4,560 tons full load
Dimensions: length 136.6m (448ft); beam 14.2m (46.6ft); draught 4.6m (15.1ft)
Gun armament: two 127mm (5in) OTO Melara Compact L/54 DP in single mountings and four 76mm (3in) OTO Melara Compact L/62 DP in single mountings
Missile armament: 40 RIM-24 Tartar and RIM-66 Standard surface-to-air missiles
Anti-submarine armament: 12 324mm (12.75in) Mk 46 A/S torpedoes, 12 A 184 A/S torpedoes and helicopter-launched torpedoes
Aircraft: two Agusta-Bell AB212 ASW
Electronics: air-search, tracking and missile guidance and surface-search radars, fire-control systems and flares/chaff launchers
Propulsion: four Foster-Wheeler boilers supplying steam to two double-reduction geared turbines (CNR in *Audace* and Ansaldo in *Ardito*) delivering 54,440kW (73,000shp) to two shafts
Performance: maximum speed 34kt; range 5,560km (3,455 miles) at 20kt
Complement: 30 + 350
Ships: two, *Audace* and *Ardito*

Both units were laid down in the 1960s, commissioned in the 1970s, and modernised in the 1980s

Charles F Adams class

Type: guided missile destroyer
Country of origin: USA
Displacement: 3,370 tons standard and 4,500 tons full load
Dimensions: length 133.2m (437ft); beam 14.3m (47ft); draught 6.1m (20ft)
Gun armament: two 127mm (5in) L/54 DP
Missile armament: two quadruple launchers for eight RGM-84A Harpoon surface-to-surface missiles, and one Mk 11 twin launcher for 42 RIM-24 Tartar surface-to-air missiles
Anti-submarine armament: one octuple launcher for RUR-5A ASROC missiles and two triple Mk 32 tube mountings for 324mm (12.75in) Mk 46 A/S torpedoes
Propulsion: four Babcock & Wilcox boilers supplying steam to two geared General Electric turbines delivering 52,200kW (70,000shp) to two shafts
Performance: maximum speed 30kt; range 11,105km (6,900 miles) at 14kt or 2,960km (1,840 miles) at 30kt
Complement: 20 + 340
Ships: 23 (USA); *Charles F Adams* + 22 and 3 (Australia) *Perth* + two

The Australian ships differ in their electronics and Ikara anti-submarine systems

County class

Type: guided missile destroyer
Country of origin: UK
Displacement: 6,200 tons standard and 6,800 tons full load
Dimensions: length 158.7m (520ft); beam 16.5m (54ft); draught 6.3m (20.5ft)
Gun armament: two 114mm (4.5in) L/45 DP and two 20mm (0.79in) Oerlikon AA
Missile armament: Exocet surface-to-surface missiles, 36 Seaslug Mk 2 surface-to-air missiles and Sea Cat surface-to-air missiles
Anti-submarine armament: 12 Mk 46 A/S torpedoes
Aircraft: one Westland Wessex HAS.Mk 3 helicopter
Propulsion: COSAG (COmbined Steam And Gas turbine) arrangement, with two Babcock & Wilcox boilers supplying steam to two sets of AEI geared turbines delivering 22,370kW (30,000shp) and four G6 gas turbines delivering 22,370kW (30,000shp) to two shafts
Performance: maximum speed 30kt; range 6,440km (4,000 miles) at 28kt
Complement: 34 + 438
Ships: four (Chile) *Capitán Prat* + three; one (Pakistan), *Barbur*

The Chilean ships were transferred between April 1982 and August 1987,
and Barbur to Pakistan in May 1982

F67 class

Type: guided missile destroyer
Country of origin: France
Displacement: 4,580 tons standard and 5,745 tons full load
Dimensions: length 152.75m (501.1ft); beam 15.3m (50.2ft); draught 5.7m (18.7ft)
Gun armament: two 100mm (3.9in) L/55 DP and two 20mm (0.79in) AA
Missile armament: Exocet surface-to-surface missiles and Crotale Naval surface-to-air missiles
Anti-submarine armament: one launcher for 13 Malafon missiles and two launchers for L5 A/S torpedoes
Electronics: air and surface-search and navigation radars, fire-control systems, search and attack sonar, a combat information system and chaff launchers
Propulsion: four boilers supplying steam to two sets of Rateau double-reduction geared turbines delivering 40,565kW (54,400shp) to two shafts
Performance: maximum speed 32kt; range 9,250km (5,750 miles) at 18kt or 3,500km (2,175 miles) at 30kt
Complement: 17 + 113 + 162
Ships: three; *Tourville* + two

Built in the 1970s, these three units are now due to be upgraded

F70/ASW class

Type: guided missile destroyer (A/S)
Country of origin: France
Displacement: 3,850 tons standard and 4,170 tons full load
Dimensions: length 139m (455.9ft); beam 14m (45.9ft); draught 5.7m (18.7ft)
Gun armament: one 100mm (3.9in) L/55 DP and two 20mm (0.79in) AA
Missile armament: four container-launchers for eight MM.38 (MM.40 from D642 onwards) Exocet surface-to-surface missiles and one octuple launcher for 26 Crotale surface-to-air missiles
Anti-submarine armament: two tubes for 10 533mm (21in) L5 torpedoes and helicopter-launched Mk 46 A/S torpedoes
Aircraft: two Westland Lynx Mk 2 helicopters
Propulsion: CODOG (COmbined Diesel Or Gas turbine) arrangement, with two Rolls-Royce Olympus TM3B gas turbines delivering 38,775kW (52,000bhp) to two shafts
Performance: maximum speed 30kt on gas turbines or 21kt on diesels; range 15,750km (9,785 miles) at 17kt
Complement: 15 + 90 + 111
Ships: seven; *Georges Leygues* + six

Illustrated is the F70/AA class escort, which was the same hull design but with a different electronics and weapons fit to the ASW

Farragut or Coontz class

Type: guided missile destroyer
Country of origin: USA
Displacement: 4,150-4,580 tons standard and 5,710-5,910 tons full load
Dimensions: length 156.3m (512.5ft); beam 16m (52.5ft); draught 7.1m (23.4ft)
Gun armament: one 127mm (5in) L/54 DP in a Mk 42 single mounting
Missile armament: two quadruple container-launchers for eight RGM-84A Harpoon surface-to-surface missiles and one Mk 10 twin launcher for 40 RIM-66D Standard SM-2 surface-to-air missiles
Anti-submarine armament: one octuple launcher for RUR-5A ASROC missiles and two triple Mk 32 tube mountings for 324mm (12.75in) Mk 46 torpedoes
Aircraft: provision for a helicopter on a platform aft
Propulsion: four Babcock & Wilcox boilers supplying steam to two Allis-Chalmers geared turbines delivering 63,385kW (85,000shp) to two shafts
Performance: maximum speed 33kt; range 9,225km (5,750 miles) at 20kt
Complement: 21 + 356 and provision for a flag staff of 7 + 12
Ships: 10; *Farragut* + nine

Improved action information systems are to be fitted

Hamburg class (Type 101A)

Type: guided missile destroyer
Country of origin: West Germany
Displacement: 3,340 tons standard and 4,680 tons full load
Dimensions: length 133.8m (439ft); beam 13.4m (44ft); draught 6.2m (20.3ft)
Gun armament: three 100mm (3.9in) L/55 DP in single mountings and eight 40mm (1.58in) Breda AA in four twin mountings
Missile armament: two twin container-launchers for MM.38 Exocet surface-to-surface missiles
Anti-submarine armament: two four-barrel Bofors 375mm (14.75in) rocket launchers, one quadruple 533mm (21in) tube mounting for A/S torpedoes and two depth-charge throwers
Propulsion: four Wahodag boilers supplying steam to two sets of geared turbines delivering 50,710kW (68,000shp) to two shafts
Performance: maximum speed 34kt; range 11,125km (6,915 miles) at 13kt or 1,700km (1,055 miles) at 34kt
Complement: 19 + 249
Ships: four; *Hamburg* + three

No longer effective, the class is
obsolescent

Hatsuyuki or Type 122 class

Type: anti-submarine and anti-ship guided missile destroyer
Country of origin: Japan
Displacement: 3,050 tons standard and 3,700 tons full load
Dimensions: length 130m (426.5ft); beam 13.6m (44.6ft); draught 4.4m (14.4ft)
Gun armament: 76mm (3in) OTO Melara L/62 DP, two 20mm (0.79in) Phalanx Mk 15
Missile armament: RGM-84 Harpoon anti-ship and RIM-7 NATO Sea Sparrow SAMs
Anti-submarine armament: 16 RUR-5A ASROC missiles, Mk 46 torpedoes and helicopter-launched weapons
Aircraft: one Mitsubishi (Sikorsky) HSS-3B Sea King helicopter in a hangar aft
Electronics: air-search and surface-search radars, fire-control systems, active search and attack hull sonar, action information system, ESM system with warning and jamming elements and chaff/flare launchers
Propulsion: COGOG arrangement, with two Kawasaki/Rolls-Royce Olympus TM3B gas turbines delivering 33,550kW (45,000shp) or two Rolls-Royce Tyne RM1C gas turbines delivering 6,890kW (9,240shp) to two shafts
Performance: speed 30kt
Complement: 195 or (DD129 onwards) 200
Ships: 12, *Hatsuyuki* +11

Impavido class

Type: guided missile destroyer
Country of origin: Italy
Displacement: 3,200 tons standard and 3,990 tons full load
Dimensions: length 131.3m (429.5ft); beam 13.6m (44.7ft); draught 4.5m (14.8ft)
Gun armament: two 127mm (5in) L/38 DP and four 76mm (3in) L/62 DP
Missile armament: 40 RIM-66 Standard surface-to-air missiles
Anti-submarine armament: 324mm (12.75in) Mk 46 torpedoes
Aircraft: provision for a light helicopter
Electronics: one RCA SPS-12 air-search radar, one Hughes SPS-52B 3D air-search radar, one SMA SPQ 2 surface-search radar, two SPG-51B missile-control radars used in conjunction with two Raytheon Mk 73 missile fire-control systems and three Selenia Orion RTN 10X gun-control radars used with the three ELSAG Argo NA10 gun fire-control systems
Propulsion: four Foster-Wheeler boilers supplying steam to two sets of Tosi geared turbines delivering 52,200kW (70,000shp) to two shafts
Performance: maximum speed 33kt; range 6,100km (3,790 miles) at 20kt
Complement: 23 + 317
Ships: two, *Impavido* and *Intrepido*

Iroquois class

Type: guided missile destroyer
Country of origin: Canada
Displacement: 3,550 tons standard and 4,700 tons full load
Dimensions: length 129.8m (426ft); beam 15.2m (50ft); draught 4.7m (15.5ft)
Gun armament: one 127mm (5in) L/54 DP OTO Melara Compact
Missile armament: 32 RIM-7 Sea Sparrow surface-to-air missiles
Anti-submarine armament: 324mm (12.75 in) Mk 46 torpedoes, one Mk NG 10 Limbo mortar and helicopter-launched weapons
Aircraft: two Sikorsky CH-124 Sea King helicopters
Propulsion: COGOG (COmbined Gas turbine Or Gas turbine) arrangement, with two Pratt & Whitney FT4A2 gas turbines delivering 37,285kW (50,000shp) or two Pratt & Whitney FT12AH3 gas turbines delivering 5,520kW (7,400shp) to two shafts
Performance: maximum speed 29+ kt on main engines or 18kt on cruising engines; range 8,370km (5,200 miles) at 20kt
Complement: 20+225, and an air unit of 7+33
Ships: four, *Iroquois* + three

The class has now been developed into dual-role area-defence and anti-submarine destroyers

Kanin class

Type: guided missile destroyer
Country of origin: USSR
Displacement: 3,700 tons standard and 4,700 tons full load
Dimensions: length 139m (455.9ft); beam 14.7m (48.2ft); draught 5m (16.4ft)
Gun armament: eight 57mm (2.25in) L/70 AA in two quadruple mountings and eight 30mm (1.18in) AA in four twin mountings
Missile armament: one twin launcher for 22 SA-N-1 'Goa' surface-to-air missiles
Torpedo armament: two quintuple 533mm (21in) AS/ASW tube mountings
Anti-submarine armament: three RBU 6000 12-barrel rocket launchers
Aircraft: provision for one helicopter on a platform aft
Propulsion: four boilers supplying steam to two sets of geared turbines delivering 59,655kW (80,000shp) to two shafts
Performance: maximum speed 34kt; range 8,350km (5,190 miles) at 16kt or 2,050km (1,275 miles) at 33kt
Complement: 350
Ships: eight; four left in service

Built between 1957 and 1962, the class is now obsolete, though two craft remain active with two more in reserve

Kashin class

Type: guided missile destroyer
Country of origin: USSR
Displacement: 3,750 tons standard and 4,500 tons full load
Dimensions: length 143.3m (470.7ft); beam 15.8m (51.8ft); draught 4.7m (15.4ft)
Gun armament: four 76mm (3in) L/60 DP in two twin mountings
Missile armament: two twin launchers for 32 SA-N-1 'Goa' surface-to-air missiles
Torpedo armament: one quintuple 533mm (21in) AS/ASW tube mounting
Anti-submarine armament: two RBU 6000 12-barrel rocket launchers and two RBU 1000 six-barrel rocket launchers
Aircraft: one Kamov Ka-25 'Hormone-A' helicopter on a platform aft
Electronics: 3D, air-search and navigation radars, and fire control systems
Propulsion: four gas turbines delivering 70,095kW (94,000shp) to two shafts
Performance: maximum speed 35kt; range 8,350km (5,190 miles) at 18kt or 2,600km (1,615 miles) at 34kt
Complement: 280
Ships: 13; *Komsomolets Ukrainy* +12

The world's first major warships to use gas-turbine propulsion

Kashin (Modified) class

Type: anti-aircraft, anti-ship and anti-submarine guided missile escort destroyer
Country of origin: USSR
Displacement: 3,950 tons standard and 4,900 tons full load
Dimensions: length 147m (482.3ft); beam 15.8m (51.8ft); draught 4.7m (15.4ft)
Gun armament: four 76mm (3in) L/60 DP and four 30mm (1.18in) ADGM-630
Missile armament: four SS-N-2C 'Styx' anti-ship missiles and 32 SA-N-1 'Goa' SAMs
Torpedo armament: Type 53 dual-role torpedoes
Anti-submarine armament: torpedoes and helicopter-launched weapons
Aircraft: provision for one Kamov Ka-25 'Hormone-A' helicopter on a platform aft
Electronics: 3D, air-search, surface search and navigation radars, fire-control systems, variable-depth sonar, two towed torpedo decoys, ESM system and four chaff launchers
Propulsion: four gas turbines delivering 70,100kW (94,020shp) to two shafts
Performance: maximum speed 37kt; range 8,350km (5,190 miles) at 18kt
Complement: 25 + 255
Ships: five (USSR); *Ognevoy* + four and one (Poland), *Warszawa*

An improvement on the basic Kashin class

Kashin II class

Type: anti-aircraft and anti-ship guided missile destroyer

Country of origin: USSR/India

Displacement: 3,950 tons standard and 4,950 tons full load

Dimensions: length 146.5m (480.5ft); beam 15.8m (51.8ft); draught 4.8m (15.7ft)

Gun armament: two 76mm (3in) L/60 DP, eight 30mm (1.18in) L/65 AA and four 30mm (1.18in) ADGM-630

Missile armament: four SS-N-2C 'Styx' anti-ship missiles and 44 SA-N-1 'Goa' SAMs

Torpedo armament: Type 54 torpedoes

Anti-submarine armament: rocket launchers, torpedoes and helicopter-launched weapons

Aircraft: one Kamov Ka-25 'Hormone-A' helicopter in a hangar aft

Electronics: medium-range air-search, air/surface search and navigation radars, fire-control systems, active search and attack sonar, ESM system and four chaff launchers

Propulsion: four gas turbines delivering 71,575kW (95,995shp) to two shafts

Performance: maximum speed 35kt; range 8,350km (5,190 miles) at 18kt or 1,675km (1,040 miles) at 35kt

Complement: 35 + 285

Ships: six (India); *Rajput* + 5

Kidd class

Type: multi-role guided missile destroyer
Country of origin: USA
Displacement: 6,950 tons light and 9,750 tons full load
Dimensions: length 171.8m (563.3ft); beam 16.8m (55ft); draught 9.1m (30ft)
Gun armament: two 127mm (5in) L/54 DP and two 20mm (0.79in) Phalanx Mk 16
Missile armament: eight RGM-84A Harpoon anti-ship missiles and 52 RIM-66C Standard SM-2 MR SAMs
Anti-submarine armament: Mk 46 torpedoes, 16 RUR-5A ASROC missiles and helicopter-launched weapons
Aircraft: two Kaman SH-2F Seasprite or one Sikorsky SH-60B Seahawk helicopter
Electronics: 3D, surface-search, navigation, illumination and tracking radars, fire-control systems, weapon direction system, Naval Tactical Data System and ESM system
Propulsion: four General Electric LM 2500 gas turbines delivering 59,655kW (80,000shp) to two shafts
Performance: maximum speed 33kt; range 14,805km (9,200 miles) at 17kt
Complement: 20 + 319
Ships: four; *Kidd, Callaghan, Scott* and *Chandler*

Virtually cruisers, they are the world's most powerful destroyers

Meko 360 class

Type: guided missile destroyer
Country of origin: West Germany/Argentina
Displacement: 2,900 tons standard and 3,360 tons full load
Dimensions: length 125.6m (412ft); beam 15m (49.2ft); draught 4.3m (14.1ft)
Gun armament: one 127mm (5in) L/54 DP OTO-Melara Compact and eight 40mm (1.58in) Breda L/70 AA in four twin mountings
Missile armament: eight Otomat surface-to-surface missiles and 24 Aspide SAMs
Anti-submarine armament: 324mm (12.75in) A244S AS torpedoes and helicopter-launched weapons
Aircraft: one helicopter in a hangar aft
Propulsion: CODOG (COmbined Diesel Or Gas turbine) arrangement, with two MTU 20V956 TB92 diesels delivering 7,455kW (10,000shp) and two Rolls-Royce Olympus TM3B gas turbines delivering 41,760kW (56,000shp) to two shafts
Fuel: diesel oil and kerosene
Performance: maximum speed 30.5kt on gas turbines; range 12,000km (7,455 miles) at cruising speed
Complement: 200
Ships: four (Argentina), *Almirante Brown, La Argentina, Heroina* and *Sarandi*

The 360 class was complemented by the Meko 140 class frigate

Sheffield or Type 42 class

Type: guided missile destroyer
Country of origin: UK
Displacement: 3,850 tons standard and 4,350 tons full load
Dimensions: length 125.6m (412ft); beam 14.3m (47ft); draught 5.8m (19ft) to screws
Gun armament: one 114mm (4.5in) L/55 DP, four 20mm (0.79in) Oerlikon AA, and two twin 30mm (1.18in) AA
Missile armament: 24 Sea Dart surface-to-air and surface-to-surface missiles
Anti-submarine armament: 324mm (12.75 in) Mk 46 A/S torpedoes and helicopter-launched weapons
Aircraft: one Westland Lynx HAS.Mk 2
Propulsion: COGOG arrangement, with two Rolls-Royce Tyne RM1A gas turbines delivering 6,340kW (8,500shp) and two Rolls-Royce Olympus TM3B gas turbines delivering 41,760kW (56,000shp) to two shafts
Performance: maximum speed 29kt on Olympus turbines or 18kt on Tyne turbines; range 7,400km (4,600 miles) at 18kt or 1,205km (750 miles) at 29kt
Complement: 24 + 229, 312 maximum
Ships: 12 (UK); *Birmingham* +11, and two (Argentina), *Hercules* + one

Heavier AA and CIWS defences were added as a result of experience in the Falklands war

Sovremenny class

Type: guided missile destroyer
Country of origin: USSR
Displacement: 6,200 tons standard and 7,800 tons full load
Dimensions: length 156m (511.8ft); beam 17.3m (56.8ft); draught 6.5ft (21.3ft)
Gun armament: four 130mm (5.1in) L/60 DP and four 30mm (1.18in) AA
Missile armament: eight SS-N-22 anti-ship missiles and 48 SA-N-7 surface-to-air missiles
Torpedo armament: two twin 533mm (21in) AS/ASW tube mountings
Anti-submarine armament: two RBU 1000 six-barrel rocket launchers
Aircraft: one Kamov Ka-25 'Hormone'
Electronics: one 'Top Steer' 3D radar, one 'Band Stand' SSM-control radar, six 'Front Dome' missile-control radars, one 'Kite Screech' main armament gun-control radar, two 'Bass Tilt' AA gun-control radars, three 'Palm Frond' navigation radars and extensive electronic countermeasures systems
Propulsion: four boilers supplying steam to two sets of turbo-pressurised turbines delivering 74,570kW (100,000shp) to two shafts
Performance: maximum speed 34kt
Complement: about 350
Ships: 14; *Sovremenny* +13

Extremely capable multi-role types, not far short of cruiser capacity

Spruance class

Type: guided missile destroyer
Country of origin: USA
Displacement: 5,830 tons standard and 7,810 tons full load
Dimensions: length 171.7m (563.2ft); beam 16.8m (55.1ft); draught 8.8m (29ft) to dome
Gun armament: two 127mm (5in) L/54 DP in two Mk 45 single mountings and two 20mm (0.79in) Phalanx Mk 15 mountings
Missile armament: two quadruple container-launchers for eight RGM-84A Harpoon surface-to-surface missiles, two quadruple container-launchers for eight BGM-109 Tomahawk surface-to-surface missiles and Mk 29 octuple launcher for RIM-7 Sea Sparrow SAMs
Anti-submarine armament: two triple Mk 32 tube mountings for 14 324mm (12.75in) Mk 46 A/S torpedoes and one octuple launcher for 24 RUR-5A ASROC missiles
Aircraft: one Sikorsky SH-3 Sea King or two Kaman SH-2 Seasprite helicopters
Propulsion: four General Electric LM 2500 gas turbines delivering 59,655kW (80,000shp) to two shafts
Performance: maximum speed 33kt; range 11,105km (6,900 miles) at 20kt
Complement: 24 + 272
Ships: 31; *Spruance* + 30

Numerically the USA's most important multi-role destroyer class

Suffren class

Type: guided missile destroyer
Country of origin: France
Displacement: 5,090 tons standard and 6,090 tons full load
Dimensions: length 157.6m (517.1ft); beam 15.54m (51ft); draught 6.1m (20ft)
Gun armament: two 100mm (3.9in) L/55 DP and four 20mm (0.79in) AA
Missile armament: four MM.38 Exocet surface-to-air missiles and 48 Masurca surface-to-air missiles
Anti-submarine armament: 13 Malafon missiles and L5 A/S torpedoes
Electronics: navigation radar, SAM-control radars, gun-control radar, hull-mounted active search and attack sonar, variable-depth sonar, combat information system, TACAN, one ESM system and two chaff launchers
Propulsion: four boilers supplying steam to two sets of Rateau double-reduction geared turbines delivering 54,065kW (72,500shp) to two shafts
Performance: maximum speed 34kt; range 9,500km (5,905 miles) at 18kt or 4,450km (2,765 miles) at 29kt
Complement: 23+332
Ships: two, *Suffren* and *Duquesne*

Designed in a primary role as escorts to the French aircraft carriers

T47 class

Type: anti-aircraft guided missile escort destroyer
Country of origin: France
Displacement: 2,750 tons standard and 3,740 tons full load
Dimensions: length 128.6m (421.9ft); beam 12.7m (41.7ft); draught 6.3m (20.7ft)
Gun armament: six 57mm (2.25in) Bofors L/60 DP
Missile armament: 40 RIM-24B Tartar and RIM-66B Standard SM-1 SAMs
Anti-submarine armament: one 375mm (14.76in) Modèle 1954 six-barrel rocket launcher and two triple 550mm (21.7in) mountings for L3 torpedoes
Electronics: 3D, air-search, surface-search and navigation radars; fire-control system, active search and attack hull sonar, action information system and ESM system with ARBR 10 warning element
Propulsion: four Indret boilers supplying steam to two sets of geared turbines delivering 47,000kW (63,035shp) to two shafts
Performance: maximum speed 32kt; range 9,250km (5,750 miles) at 18kt or 2,225km (1,385 miles) at 32kt
Complement: 17 + 260 in peace, 320 in war
Ships: one, *Du Chayla*

Type 82 class

Type: guided missile cruiser
Country of origin: UK
Displacement: 6,100 tons standard and 7,100 tons full load
Dimensions: length 154.5m (507ft); beam 16.8m (55ft); draught 7m (23ft) to sonar dome
Gun armament: one 114mm (4.5in) L/55 DP in one Mk 8 single mounting and two 20mm (0.79mm) Oerlikon AA in two Mk 7 single mountings
Missile armament: one twin launcher for 40 Sea Dart surface-to-air missiles
Anti-submarine armament: one launcher for 40 Ikara missiles, one Limbo Mk 10 mortar and helicopter-launched weapons
Aircraft: one Westland Wasp HAS.Mk1 helicopter on a platform aft
Propulsion: COSAG (COmbined Steam And Gas turbine) arrangement, with two boilers supplying steam to two sets of Admiralty Standard Range turbines delivering 22,370kW (30,000 shp) and two Rolls-Royce Olympus TM1A gas turbines delivering 22,370kW (30,000shp) to two shafts
Performance: maximum speed 28kt; range 9,255km (5,750 miles) at 18kt
Complement: 29 + 378
Ships: one, *Bristol*

The Bristol *remains the sole Type 82 unit*

Tachikaze or Type 168 class

Type: guided missile destroyer
Country of origin: Japan
Displacement: 3,850 tons or (DD170) 3,900 tons standard and 4,800 tons full load
Dimensions: length 143m (469.2ft); beam 14.3m (46.9ft); draught 4.6m (15ft)
Gun armament: two 127mm (5in) L/54 DP and two 20mm (0.79in) Phalanx Mk 15 CIWS mountings
Missile armament: eight RGM-84 Harpoon anti-ship missiles and 40 RIM-66B Standard SM-1 MR SAMs
Anti-submarine armament: 16 RUR-5A ASROC missiles and Mk 46 torpedoes
Electronics: 3D, air-search and surface-search radars; fire-control systems, active search and attack hull sonar, ESM system with warning and jamming elements and four chaff/flare launchers
Propulsion: two boilers supplying steam to two sets of Mitsubishi geared turbines delivering 52,200kW (70,010shp) to two shafts
Performance: maximum speed 32kt
Complement: 250
Ships: three, *Tachikaze*, *Asakaze* and *Sawakaze*

Compact and balanced craft with good all-round capability

Takatsuki or Type 164 class

Type: dual-role guided missile destroyer
Country of origin: Japan
Displacement: 3,250 tons or (DD166/167) 3,100 tons standard and 4,500 tons full load
Dimensions: length 136m (446.2ft); beam 13.4m (44ft); draught 4.4m (14.5ft)
Gun armament: 127mm (5in) L/54 DP
Missile armament: RGM-84 Harpoon anti-ship missiles and RIM-7 Sea Sparrow SAMs
Anti-submarine armament: 16 RUR-5A ASROC missiles, one 375mm (14.76in) Bofors Type 71 four-barrel rocket launcher, Mk 46 torpedoes and helicopter-launched weapons
Aircraft: provision for one helicopter
Electronics: air-search and surface-search radars, fire-control system, active search and attack hull sonar, ESM system with NOLQ-6C warning element and chaff/flare launchers
Propulsion: two Foster-Wheeler or (DD166/167) Mitsubishi boilers supplying steam to two sets of Kawasaki/General Electric or (DD166/167) Mitsubishi/Westinghouse geared turbines delivering 44,750kW (60,020shp) to two shafts
Performance: maximum speed 31kt or (DD166/167) 32kt; range 12,975km (8,065 miles) at 20kt
Complement: 260 or (DD166/167) 270
Ships: four; *Takatsuki, Kikuzuki, Mochizuki* and *Nagatsuki*

Tromp class

Type: guided missile destroyer
Country of origin: Netherlands
Displacement: 3,900 tons standard and 4,580 tons full load
Dimensions: length 138.2m (453.3ft); beam 14.8m (48.6ft); draught 4.6m (15.1ft)
Gun armament: two 120mm (4.7in) L/50 DP
Missile armament: 16 RGM-84A Harpoon surface-to-surface missiles, 40 RIM-24B Tartar surface-to-air missiles and 16 RIM-7 Sea Sparrow surface-to-air missiles
Anti-submarine armament: 324mm (12.75 in) Mk 46 A/S torpedoes
Aircraft: one Westland Lynx helicopter
Electronics: 3D, surface-search and navigation radars, hull-mounted sonar, action-data system, underwater weapon fire-control system and two chaff launchers
Propulsion: COGOG (COmbined Gas turbine Or Gas turbine) arrangement, with two Rolls-Royce Tyne TM1 gas turbines delivering 5,965kW (8,000shp) and two Rolls-Royce Olympus TM3B gas turbines delivering 37,285kW (50,000shp) to two shafts
Performance: maximum speed 30kt; range 9,250km (5,750 miles) at 18kt
Complement: 34 + 267
Ships: two, *Tromp* and *De Ruyter*

Both craft are now in need of updating

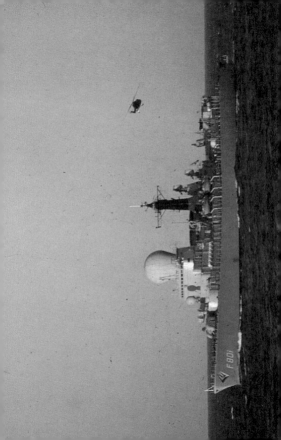

Udaloy class

Type: guided missile escort destroyer
Country of origin: USSR
Displacement: 6,700 tons standard and 8,200 tons full load
Dimensions: length 162m (531.5ft); beam 19.3m (63.3ft); draught 6.2m (20.3ft)
Gun armament: two 100mm (3.9in) DP and four 30mm (1.18in) AA in 'Gatling' mountings
Missile armament: eight SS-N-14 surface-to-underwater and surface-to-surface missiles and 48 SA-N-8 surface-to-air missiles
Torpedo armament: two quadruple 533mm (21in) AS/ASW tube mountings
Anti-submarine armament: rocket launchers, SS-N-14 missiles and helicopter-launched weapons
Aircraft: two Kamov Ka-27 'Helix-A'
Electronics: air-search, missile control, main armament gun-control and navigation radars; bow-mounted sonar, variable-depth sonar and extensive electronic countermeasure systems
Propulsion: COGOG (COmbined Gas turbine Or Gas turbine) arrangement, with four gas turbines delivering a total of about 70,000kW (93,870kW) to two shafts
Performance: maximum speed 35kt
Complement: about 350
Ships: 13 (2); *Udaloy* +12

Escort destroyers to partner the Sovremenny class

Allen M Sumner class

Type: gun destroyer
Country of origin: USA/Taiwan
Displacement: 2,200 tons standard and 3,320 tons full load
Dimensions: length 114.8m (376.5ft); beam 12.5m (40.9ft); draught 5.8m (19ft)
Gun armament: six 127mm (5in) L/38 mountings and four 76mm (3in) L/50 in two twin Mk 38 mountings
Missile armament: four MM.38 Exocet surface-to-surface missiles in single launchers
Anti-submarine armament: two triple ILAS 3 tube mountings for 324mm (12.75in) Whitehead A 244S A/S torpedoes and two forward-firing Hedgehog mortars
Propulsion: four Babcock & Wilcox boilers supplying steam to two geared turbines delivering 44,740kW (60,000shp) to two shafts
Performance: maximum speed 34kt; range 8,530km (5,300 miles) at 15kt or 1,835km (1,140 miles) at 31kt
Complement: 331
Ships: one (Brazil) *Mato Grosso*; six (Taiwan), *Hsiang Yang* + five

Allen M Sumner (FRAM II) class

Type: gun destroyer
Country of origin: USA/Brazil
Displacement: 2,200 tons standard and 3,320 tons full load
Dimensions: length 114.8m (376.5ft); beam 12.5m (40.9ft); draught 5.8m (19ft)
Gun armament: six 127mm (5in) L/38 DP
Anti-submarine armament: Mk 46 torpedoes, two Hedgehog rocket launchers and helicopter-launched weapons
Aircraft: provision for one Westland Wasp HAS.Mk1 light helicopter in a hangar aft
Electronics: air-search and surface-search radar, gun fire-control system, active search and attack sonar and variable-depth sonar, underwater weapons fire-control system and ESM system with warning and jamming elements
Propulsion: four Babcock & Wilcox boilers supplying steam to two sets of geared turbines delivering 44,740kW (60,000shp) to two shafts
Performance: maximum speed 34kt; range 8,530km (5,300 miles) at 15kt
Complement: 15+253
Ships: four (Brazil), *Sergipe* + three; two (Chile), *Ministro Zenteno* + one; one (Greece), *Minoulis*; two (Iran), *Badr* and *Palang*; two (South Korea), *Dae Gu* and *Inchon*; two (Taiwan), *Lo Yang* and *Nan Yung*; one (Turkey), *Zafaer*

Carpenter (FRAM I) class

Type: gun destroyer
Country of origin: USA/Turkey
Displacement: 2,425 tons standard and 3,540 tons full load
Dimensions: length 119m (390ft 6in); beam 12.5m (41ft); draught 6.4m (20ft 10.5in)
Gun armament: two 127mm (5in) L/38 DP in a Mk 38 twin mounting, two 76mm (3in) L/50 DP in a twin mounting and two 35mm (1.376in) Oerlikon L/90 AA in a GDM-A twin mounting
Anti-submarine armament: one Mk 16 octuple launcher for eight RUR-5A ASROC missiles; two Mk 32 triple 324mm (12.75in) mountings for Mk 46 torpedoes; helicopter-launched weapons and one rack for depth charges
Aircraft: provision for one Agusta-Bell AB.212 ASW on a platform aft
Electronics: one SPS-40 air-search, one surface search radar and one gun fire-control system
Propulsion: four Babcock & Wilcox boilers supplying steam to two sets of General Electric geared turbines delivering 44,740kW (60,000shp) to two shafts
Performance: maximum speed 33kt; range 7,945km (6,900 miles) at 12kt
Complement: 15 + 280
Ships: two (Turkey), *Alcitepe* and *Anittepe*

Kotlin and Kotlin (Modified) Class

Type: gun destroyer
Country of origin: USSR
Displacement: 2,850 tons standard and 3,600 tons full load
Dimensions: length 126.5m (414.9ft); beam 12.9m (42.3ft); draught 4.6m (15.1ft)
Gun armament: four 130mm (5.1in) L/58 DP, 16 45mm (1.78in) L/85 AA and four or eight 25mm (0.95in) L/80 AA
Torpedo armament: Type 53 torpedoes
Anti-submarine armament: two 16-barrel rocket launchers, six-barrel rocket launchers, torpedoes, depth-charge racks and throwers
Mines: 56
Aircraft: one Kamov Ka-25 'Hormone-A' helicopter on a platform aft (in one craft only)
Electronics: surface-search and navigation radars, fire-control radar, active search and attack hull sonar and ESM system
Propulsion: four boilers supplying steam to two sets of geared turbines delivering 53,700kW (72,020shp) to two shafts
Performance: maximum speed 36kt; range 8,350km (5,190 miles) at 15kt or 2,050km (1,275 miles) at 35kt
Complement: 285
Ships: Kotlin class; four, *Spleshny* + three; Kotlin (Modified) class; seven, *Blagorodny* + six

Typical destroyers of the 1950s; the
130 *class is now obsolete*

Minegumo class

Type: gun destroyer
Country of origin: Japan
Displacement: 2,050 tons standard and 2,150 tons full load
Dimensions: length 114.9m (377ft); beam 11.8m (38.7ft); draught 4m (13.1ft)
Gun armament: four 76mm (3in) L/50 DP in two Mk 33 twin mountings
Anti-submarine armament: two triple Type 68 tube mountings for 324mm (12.75in) Mk 44/46 A/S torpedoes, one Mk 16 octuple launcher for RUR-5A ASROC missiles and one Bofors Type 71 four- barrel rocket launcher
Electronics: one OPS-11 air-search radar, one OPS-17 surface-search radar, two Mk 35 gun-control radars used in conjunction with Mk 56 and Mk 63 gun fire-control systems and one OQS-3 hull-mounted sonar
Propulsion: six Mitsubishi diesels delivering 19,760kW (26,500bhp) to two shafts
Performance: maximum speed 27kt; range 12,975km (8,065 miles) at 20kt
Complement: 210
Ships: three, *Minegumo*, *Natsugumo* and *Murakumo*

Now outdated and of little use in their anti-submarine role

A69 or d'Estienne d'Orves class

Type: guided missile frigate
Country of origin: France
Displacement: 950 tons standard and 1,170 tons (or 1,250 tons in later ships) full load
Dimensions: length 80m (262.5ft); beam 10.3m (33.8ft); draught 5.3m (17.4ft) to sonar dome and 3m (9.8ft) to keel
Gun armament: one 100mm (3.9in) L/55 and two 20mm (0.79in) AA
Anti-submarine armament: one Mk 54 sextuple 375mm (14.76in) rocket launcher and four tubes for 550mm (21.65in) L3 or 533mm (21in) L5 torpedoes
Propulsion: two SEMT-Pielstick PCV diesels delivering 8,950kW (12,000bhp) to two shafts
Performance: maximum speed 24kt; range 8,340km (5,185 miles) at 15kt; endurance 15 days
Complement: 5 + 29 + 45
Ships: three (Argentina), *Drummond*, *Guerrico* and *Granville*; 17 (France), *d'Estienne d'Orves* + 16

Having been refitted, the Estienne d'Orves class carries significant anti-ship capabilities

Amazon or Type 21 class

Type: guided-missile frigate
Country of origin: UK
Displacement: 2,750 tons standard and 3,250+ tons full load
Dimensions: length 117m (384ft); beam 12.7m (41.7ft); draught 5.9m (19.5ft)
Gun armament: one 114mm (4.5in) L/55 and two 20mm (0.79in) Oerlikon cannon
Missile armament: four MM.38 Exocet surface-to-surface missiles and Sea Cat SAMs
Anti-submarine armament: 324mm (12.75 in) Mk 46 A/S torpedoes and helicopter-launched torpedoes
Aircraft: one Westland Wasp HAS.Mk1 or Westland Lynx HAS.Mk 2 helicopter
Propulsion: COGOG (COmbined Gas turbine Or Gas turbine) system, with two Rolls-Royce Olympus TM3B gas turbines delivering 41,760kW (56,000bhp) or two Rolls-Royce Tyne RM1A gas turbines delivering 6,340kW (8,500shp) to two shafts
Performance: maximum speed 30kt on Olympus turbines or 18kt on Tyne turbines; range 7,400km (4,600 miles) at 17kt or 2,220km (1,380 miles) at 30kt
Complement: 13+162, with a maximum of 192
Ships: six; *Amazon* + five

Originally a class of eight ships, two were sunk in the Falklands War

Bremen or Type 122 class

Type: guided-missile frigate
Country of origin: West Germany
Displacement: 3,415 tons full load
Dimensions: length 130.5m (428.1ft); beam 14.4m (48.5ft); draught 6m (19.7ft)
Gun armament: two quadruple launchers for eight RGM-84A Harpoon surface-to-surface missiles, one eight-cell launcher for RIM-7 Sea Sparrow surface-to-air missiles, two multiple launchers for FIM-92 Stinger surface-to-air missiles and two launchers for RAM SAMs
Anti-submarine armament: two twin Mk 32 tube mountings for 324mm (12.75in) Mk 44/46 A/S torpedoes and helicopter-launched weapons
Aircraft: two Westland Lynx helicopters
Propulsion: CODOG (COmbined Diesel Or Gas turbine) arrangement, with two General Electric LM 2500 gas turbines delivering 38.480kW (51,600shp) or two MTU 20V-956-TB92 diesels delivering 7.755kW (10.400shp) to two shafts
Performance: maximum speed 32 kts on gas turbines or 20kt on diesels; range 7.400km (4,600 miles) at 18kt
Complement: 203, with a maximum of 225 possible
Ships: eight, *Bremen* + seven

Highly capable frigates ideally designed for North Sea patrols

Broadsword Batch 1 & 2 or Type 22 Batch 1 & 2 class

Type: guided missile escort frigate
Country of origin: UK
Displacement: 3,500 tons standard and 4,000 tons full load
Dimensions: length 131.2m (430ft); beam 14.8m (48.5ft); draught 6m (19.9ft)
Gun armament: two 40mm (1.58in) Bofors L/60 AA
Missile armament: MM.38 Exocet surface-to-surface missiles and Sea Wolf SAMs
Anti-submarine armament: helicopter-launched torpedoes
Aircraft: two Westland Lynx HAS.Mk 2 helicopters
Propulsion: COGOG (COmbined Gas turbine Or Gas turbine) arrangement, with two Rolls-Royce Olympus TM3B gas turbines delivering 41,760kW (56,000shp) or two Rolls-Royce Tyne RM1A gas turbines delivering 6,340kW (8,500shp) to two shafts
Performance: maximum speed 30kt on Olympus engines, and 18kt on Tyne engines; range 8,370km (5,200 miles) at 18kt on Tyne engines
Complement: 18 + 205, with a maximum of 296 possible
Ships: Batch 1 four, *Broadsword* + three; Batch 2 six, *Boxer* + five

Rated as frigates, but they are destroyers ideally suited to anti-submarine operations

140

Broadsword Batch 3 or Cornwall class

Type: multi-role guided missile escort frigate
Country of origin: UK
Displacement: 4,200 tons standard and 4,900 tons full load
Dimensions: length 148.1m (485.9ft); beam 14.8m (48.5ft); draught 6.4m (21ft)
Gun armament: one 114mm (4.5in) L/55 DP, two 30mm (1.18in) Oerlikon L/75 DP and one 30mm (1.18in) Goalkeeper CIWS mounting
Missile armament: eight RGM-84 Harpoon anti-ship missiles and 60 Sea Wolf SAMs
Anti-submarine armament: torpedoes
Aircraft: two Westland Lynx HAS.Mk 2 helicopters; can also embark two EH.101 or Westland Sea King HAS.Mk 5/6 helicopters
Electronics: air-search, surface-search and navigation radars, fire-control systems, search and attack hull sonar, action information system and warning and jamming ESM system
Propulsion: COGAG system, two Rolls-Royce Spey SM1A gas turbines delivering 27,995kW (37,450shp) and two Rolls-Royce Tyne RM3C gas turbines delivering 7,230kW (9,700shp) to two shafts
Performance: maximum speed 30kt on Spey engines, and 18kt on Tyne engines; range 8,370km (5,200 miles) at 18kt on Tyne engines
Complement: 31 + 219, maximum 301
Ships: four, *Cornwall* + three

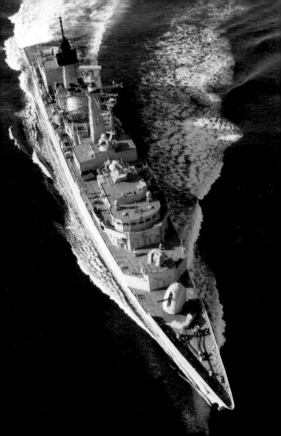

Brooke class

Type: anti-submarine and anti-aircraft guided missile escort frigate
Country of origin: USA
Displacement: 2,645 tons standard and 3,425 tons full load
Dimensions: length 126.3m (414.5ft); beam 13.5m (44.2ft); draught 4.6m (15ft)
Gun armament: one 127mm (5in) L/38 DP
Missile armament: 16 RIM-66B Standard SM-1 MR SAMs
Anti-submarine armament: eight or 16 RUR-5A ASROC missiles, Mk 46 torpedoes and helicopter-launched weapons
Aircraft: one Kaman SH-2F Seasprite helicopter in a hangar aft
Electronics: 3D, surface-search and navigation radar, fire-control system, one active search and attack bow sonar, weapon direction system, ESM system with warning and jamming elements and four chaff/flare launchers
Propulsion: two Foster-Wheeler boilers supplying steam to one set of Westinghouse or (last three ships) General Electric geared turbines delivering 26,100kW (35,000shp) to one shaft
Performance: maximum speed 27.2kt; range 7,400km (4,600 miles) at 20kt
Complement: 17 + 260
Ships: four (Pakistan), *Saif* + three

Decommissioned by the US Navy and transferred to Pakistan in 1989

Commandant Rivière class

Type: guided missile escort frigate
Country of origin: France
Displacement: 1,750 tons standard and 2,250 tons full load
Dimensions: length 103m (337.9ft); beam 11.5m (37.7ft); draught 4.3m (14.1ft)
Gun armament: two 100mm (3.9in) L/55 DP in single mountings and two 30mm (1.18in) AA
Missile armament: MM.38 Exocet surface-to-surface missiles
Anti-submarine armament: L3 or K2 torpedoes and one quadruple 305mm (12in) mortar
Aircraft: provision for one light helicopter
Electronics: air-search and air/surface search radars, Thomson-CSF DRBC 32A gun-control radar, Thomson-CSF DRBC 32C missile-control, navigation radar, hull-mounted sonar and two CSEE Dagaie chaff launchers
Propulsion: four SEMT-Pielstick diesels delivering 11,930kW (16,000shp) to two shafts
Performance: maximum speed 25kt; range 11,100km (6,700miles) at 10-12kt
Complement: 10 + 61 + 96, and accommodation for a detachment of 80 troops who can be landed in two specially-carried LCPs
Ships: seven (France), *Commandant Bory* + six; one (Uruguay) *General Artigas*

Commissioned in the early 1960s, one transferred to Uruguay in 1989

Descubierta or F30 class

Type: guided missile escort frigate
Country of origin: Spain
Displacement: 1,235 tons standard and 1,480 tons full load
Dimensions: length 88.8m (291.3ft); beam 10.4m (34ft); draught 3.8m (12.5ft)
Gun armament: one 76mm (3in) OTO Melara L/62 DP, one 40mm (1.58in) Bofors L/70 AA and one 20mm (0.79in) Meroka CIWS
Missile armament: eight RGM-84 Harpoon anti-ship and 24 RIM-7 Sea Sparrow SAMs
Anti-submarine armament: Mk 46 torpedoes and one 375mm (14.76in) Bofors twin-barrel rocket launcher
Electronics: air/surface search, surface-search and navigation radars; fire-control systems, active search and attack hull sonar, action information system, and ESM system
Propulsion: four MTU/Bazan 16V 956 TB91 diesels delivering 13,400kW (17,970shp) to two shafts
Performance: maximum speed 25.5kt; range 7,400km (4,600 miles) at 18kt
Complement: 10+108 and provision for 30 marines
Ships: two (Egypt), *El Suez* and *Abu Qir*; one (Morocco), *Colonel Errhamani*; and six (Spain), *Descubierta* + five

Based on the Portuguese-designed João Coutinho class

Duke or Type 23 class

Type: multi-role guided missile frigate
Country of origin: UK
Displacement: 3,500 tons standard and 4,200 tons full load
Dimensions: length 133m (436.2ft); beam 16.1m (52.8ft); draught 5.5m (18ft)
Gun armament: 114mm (4.5in) Vickers L/55 DP and 30mm (1.18in) Oerlikon L/75 AA
Missile armament: eight RGM-84 Harpoon anti-ship missiles and 32 Sea Wolf SAMs
Anti-submarine armament: Stingray torpedoes and helicopter launched weapons
Aircraft: one or two Westland Lynx HAS.Mk 2/3 or one EH.101 helicopter in a hangar aft
Electronics: 3D and navigation radar, fire-control system, active search and attack bow sonar, action information system, ESM system with warning and jamming elements and four Sea Gnat chaff/decoy launchers
Propulsion: CODAG system, two Rolls-Royce Spey SM1A gas turbines delivering 25,355kW (34,000shp) and four Paxman Valenta 12 RPA 200 CZ diesels delivering 5,220kW (7,000shp) to two shafts
Performance: maximum speed 28kt; range 14,485km (9,000 miles) at 15kt
Complement: 12+134 with a maximum of 17+168 possible
Ships: seven; *Norfolk* + six

F2000S or Al Madinah class

Type: dual-role guided missile frigate
Country of origin: France/Saudi Arabia
Displacement: 2,000 tons standard and 2,870 tons full load
Dimensions: length 115m (377.3ft); beam 12.5m (41ft); draught 4.7m (15.3ft)
Gun armament: 100mm (3.9in) Creusot Loire L/55 DP, 40mm (1.58in) Breda L/70 AA
Missile armament: eight Otomat Mk 2 anti-ship missiles and 26 Matra R.440 SAMs
Anti-submarine armament: F17P wire-guided torpedoes and Mk 46 torpedoes
Aircraft: one Aérospatiale SA 365F Dauphin 2 helicopter in a hangar aft
Electronics: air/surface search and navigation radars, gun fire-control system, weapon direction system, active search and attack hull sonar, action information system with Erato for Otomat control, ESM system with warning and jamming elements, direction finding system, two chaff/flare launchers and satellite navigation system
Propulsion: CODAD (COmbined Diesel And Diesel) arrangement, with four SEMT-Pielstick 16 PA6-V280 BTC diesels delivering 24,240kW (32,510shp) to two shafts
Performance: maximum speed 30kt; range 12,000km (7,455 miles) at 18kt
Complement: 15 + 164
Ships: four (Saudi Arabia), *Al Madinah* + three

Ishikari or Type 226 class

Type: anti-ship and anti-submarine guided missile frigate
Country of origin: Japan
Displacement: 1,290 tons standard and 1,450 tons full load
Dimensions: length 85m (278.8ft); beam 10.6m (34.7ft); draught 5.9m (19.2ft)
Gun armament: one 76mm (3in) OTO Melara L/62 DP in an OTO Melara Compact single mounting
Missile armament: eight RGM-84 Harpoon anti-ship missiles
Anti-submarine armament: one 375mm (14.76in) Bofors Type 71 four-barrel rocket launcher and two Type 68 triple 324mm (12.75in) mountings for Mk 46 torpedoes
Electronics: surface-search and navigation radar, gun fire-control system, active search and attack hull sonar, ESM system with warning and jamming elements and chaff/flare launcher
Propulsion: CODOG (COmbined Diesel Or Gas turbine) arrangement, with one Kawasaki/Rolls-Royce Olympus TM3B gas turbine delivering 21,570kW (28,930shp) or one Mitsubishi 6 DRV 35/44 diesel delivering 3,500kW (4,695shp) to two shafts
Performance: maximum speed 25kt
Complement: 90
Ships: one, *Ishikari*

Knox class

Type: dual-role guided missile escort frigate
Country of origin: USA
Displacement: 3,010 tons standard and 3,875 tons or (FF1078/1097) 4,260 tons full load
Dimensions: length 133.5m (438ft); beam 14.3m (46.8ft); draught 7.8m (24.8ft)
Gun armament: one 127mm (5in) L/54 DP and one 20mm (0.79in) Phalanx Mk 15 CIWS
Missile armament: anti-ship missiles
Anti-submarine armament: RUR-5A ASROC missiles, torpedoes and helicopter-launched weapons
Aircraft: one Kaman SH-2F Seasprite
Electronics: air-search, surface-search and navigation radars, fire-control system, weapon direction system, active search and attack bow sonar, target designation system, ESM system with warning and jamming elements, chaff/flare launchers and satellite communications system
Propulsion: two Combustion Engineering or Babcock & Wilcox boilers supplying steam to one set of Westinghouse geared turbines delivering 26,100kW (35,000shp)
Performance: maximum speed 27kt; range 8,370km (5,200 miles) at 20kt
Complement: 17+121
Ships: five (Spain), Baleares or F70 class, and 46 USA, Knox +45

The largest Western postwar class
until Oliver Hazard Perry *in 1977*

Koni class

Type: guided missile frigate
Country of origin: USSR
Displacement: 1,700 tons standard and 2,000 tons full load
Dimensions: length 95m (311.6ft); beam 12m (39.3ft); draught 4.2m (13.7ft)
Gun armament: four 76mm (3in) L/60 DP in two twin mountings and four 30mm (1.18in) AA in two twin mountings
Missile armament: one twin launcher for SA-N-4 surface-to- air missiles
Anti-submarine armament: two RBU 6000 12-barrel rocket launchers
Propulsion: CODAG (COmbined Diesel And Gas turbine) arrangement, with two diesels delivering 8,950kW (12,000shp) and one gas turbine delivering 13,425kW (18,000shp) to three shafts
Performance): maximum speed 28kt on gas turbine and 22kt on diesels; range 3,700km (2,300 miles) at 14kt
Complement: 110
Ships: three (Algeria), *Murat Rais*, *Rais Kellich* and *Rais Korfo*; three (Cuba); three (East Germany), *Rostock*, *Berlin* and *Halle*; two (Libya), *Al Hani* and *Al Qirdabiyah*; one (USSR), *Delfin*; four (Yugoslavia), *Split*, *Koper*, *Kotor* and *Pula*

A single Type I is retained by Russia for training foreign crews; all other Koni class frigates were Type II or III

Kortenaer class

Type: guided missile frigate
Country of origin: Netherlands
Displacement: 3,050 tons standard and 3,630 tons full load
Dimensions: length 130.5m (428.1ft); beam 14.4m (47.2ft); draught 6.2m (20.3ft) to the screws
Gun armament: one 76mm (3in) L/62 DP OTO Melara Compact and one 40mm (1.58in) Bofors AA (to be replaced by Hollandse Signaalapparaten close-in cannon system)
Missile armament: eight RGM-84A Harpoon surface-to-surface missiles and RIM-7 Sea Sparrow surface-to-air missiles
Anti-submarine armament: Mk 46 A/S torpedoes and helicopter-launched weapons
Aircraft: two Westland Lynx helicopters
Propulsion: COGOG (COmbined Gas turbine Or Gas turbine) arrangement, with two Rolls-Royce Olympus TM3B gas turbines delivering 37,285kW (50,000shp) or two Rolls-Royce Tyne RMIC gas turbines delivering 5,965kW (8,000shp) to two shafts
Performance: maximum speed 30kt, range 8,700km (5,405 miles) on Tyne engines at 16kt
Complement: 167
Ships: two (Greece), *Elli* and *Limnos*; 10 (Netherlands), *Kortenaer* + nine

Now undergoing extensive
160 *modernisation*

Krivak I, Krivak II, and Krivak III class

Type: multi-role guided missile escort frigate
Country of origin: USSR
Displacement: 3,000 tons standard and 3,700 tons or (II and III class) 3,900 tons full load
Dimensions: length 123.5m (405.2ft); beam 14m (45.9ft); draught 5m (16.4ft)
Gun armament: four 76mm (3in) L/60 DP and two 30mm (1.18in) ADGM-630 CIWS
Missile armament: SA-N-4 'Gecko' SAMs
Torpedo armament: Type 53 torpedoes
Anti-submarine armament: four SS-N-14 'Silex' missiles (not in Krivak III class), and two RBU 6000 12-barrel rocket launchers
Mines: 30/40, depending on type
Aircraft: one Kamov Ka-27 'Helix-A' helicopter in a hangar aft (Krivak III class only)
Electronics: extensive radar and electronic control systems, sonar and decoy systems
Propulsion: COGAG arrangement, with two gas turbines delivering 41,000kW (54,980shp) and two gas turbines delivering 10,500kW (14,085shp) to two shafts
Performance: maximum speed 32kt; range 7,400km (4,600 miles) at 15kt
Complement: 180
Ships: 21 Krivak I class, 11 Krivak II class and six Krivak III class

Krivak I craft (right) were built from 1970, Krivak IIs from 1976 and the first Krivak III appeared in 1984

Leander Batch 2 TA class

Type: dual-role guided missile frigate
Country of origin: UK
Displacement: 2,450 tons standard and 3,200 tons full load
Dimensions: length 113.4m (372ft); beam 12.5m (41ft); draught 5.8m (19ft)
Gun armament: 20mm (0.79in) Oerlikon AA
Missile armament: four MM.38 Exocet anti-ship missiles and Sea Cat SAMs
Anti-submarine armament: Mk 46 or Stingray torpedoes (being removed) and helicopter-launched weapons
Aircraft: one Westland Lynx HAS.Mk 2/3 helicopter in a hangar aft
Electronics: air/surface-search and navigation radars, fire-control system, active search and attack hull sonar, passive search towed-array sonar, action information system, ESM system with warning and jamming elements, chaff launchers and satellite communications system
Propulsion: two Babcock & Wilcox boilers supplying steam to two sets of White/English Electric geared turbines delivering 22,370kW (30,000shp) to two shafts
Performance: maximum speed 28kt; range 7,400km (4,600 miles) at 15kt
Complement: 18 + 248
Ships: two (New Zealand), *Waikato* and *Southland*; eight (UK), *Cleopatra* + seven

Leander Batch 3 or Broad-Beam Leander class

Type: anti-ship guided missile frigate
Country of origin: UK
Displacement: 2,500 tons standard and 2,960 tons full load
Dimensions: length 113.4m (372ft); beam 131.1m (43ft); draught 5.5m (18ft) to screws
Gun armament: two 114mm (4.5in) L/45 DP in one Mk 6 twin mounting and two 20mm (0.79in) AA in single mountings
Missile armament: one quadruple launcher for Sea Cat surface-to-air missiles, and one sextuple launcher for Sea Wolf surface-to-air missiles
Anti-submarine armament: one Limbo three-barrel mortar
Aircraft: one Westland Lynx HAS.Mk 2 helicopter
Propulsion: two Babcock & Wilcox boilers supplying steam to two sets of White/English Electric double-reduction geared turbines delivering 22,370kW (30,000shp) to two shafts
Performance: maximum speed 28kt; range 7,400km (4,600 miles) at 15kt
Complement: 19 + 241
Ships: three (Chile), *Candell, Almirante Lynch, ex-Achilles;* two (New Zealand), *Canterbury* and *Wellington;* two (Pakistan), *Shansher* and *Zulfiqar;* and six (UK), *Andromeda* + five

The Broad-Beam Leander is 0.6m
(24in) wider than the Batch 2 TA

Lupo class

Type: guided missile frigate
Country of origin: Italy
Displacement: 2,210 tons standard and 2,500 tons full load
Dimensions: length 113.2m (371.3ft); beam 11.3m (37.1ft); draught 3.7m (12.1ft)
Gun armament: one 127mm (5in) L/54 DP and four 40mm (1.58in) Breda AA
Missile armament: eight Otomat Mk 2 surface-to-surface missiles and RIM-7 Sea Sparrow surface-to-air missiles
Anti-submarine armament: Mk 44/46 A/S torpedoes and helicopter-launched weapons
Aircraft: one helicopter in a hangar aft
Propulsion: CODOG (COmbined Diesel Or Gas turbine) arrangement, with two General Motors diesels delivering 5,815kW (7,800shp) or two Fiat/General Electric LM 2500 gas turbines delivering 37,285kW (50,000shp) to two shafts
Performance: maximum speed 35kt on gas turbines or 21kt on diesels; range 8,000km (4,970 miles) at 16kt on diesels
Complement: 16 + 169
Ships: four (Iraq), *Hittin* + three; four (Italy), *Lupo* + three; four (Peru), *Meliton Carrajal* + three; six (Venezuela), *Mariscal Sucre* + five

The Italian Navy quickly dropped the Lupo class in favour of the Maestrale class

Maestrale class

Type: guided missile frigate
Country of origin: Italy
Displacement: 2,500 tons standard and 3,040 tons full load
Dimensions: length 122.7m (405ft); beam 12.9m (42.5ft); draught 8.4m (27.4ft) to screws
Gun armament: one 127mm (5in) L/54 DP and four 40mm (1.58in) Breda L/70 AA
Missile armament: four Otomat Mk 2 surface-to-surface missiles and Aspide SAMs
Torpedo armament: A 184 wire-guided anti-ship and anti-submarine torpedoes
Anti-submarine armament: Mk 44/46 A/S torpedoes and helicopter-launched weapons
Aircraft: two Agusta-Bell AB.212 ASW helicopters
Propulsion: CODOG arrangement, with two General Motors 230 diesels delivering 8,200kW (11,000shp) or two Fiat/General Electric LM 2500 gas turbines delivering 37,285kW (50,000shp) to two shafts
Performance: maximum speed 32kt on gas turbines and 21kt on diesels; range 11,125km (6,915 miles) at 16kt
Complement: 24 + 208
Ships: eight, *Maestrale* + seven

Developed from the Lupo class, the Maestrale ships combine better seakeeping with better anti-submarine weaponry

Meko 360H2 class

Type: dual-role guided missile frigate
Country of origin: West Germany/Nigeria
Displacement: 3,630 tons full load
Dimensions: length 125.6m (412ft); beam 15m (49.2ft); draught 4.3m (14.1ft)
Gun armament: one 127mm (5in) OTO Melara L/54 DP and eight 40mm (1.58in) Bofors L/70 AA
Missile armament: eight Otomat anti-ship missiles and 24 Aspide SAMs
Anti-submarine armament: A 244/S torpedoes, one depth-charge rack and helicopter-launched weapons
Aircraft: one Westland Lynx Mk 89 helicopter
Electronics: air/surface search, navigation and gun fire-control radars, active search and attack hull sonar, ESM system with warning and jamming elements and chaff/flare launchers
Propulsion: CODOG arrangement, with two Rolls-Royce Olympus TM3B gas turbines delivering 41,760kW (56,000shp) or two MTU 20V 956 TB92 diesels delivering 7,500kW (10,060shp) to two shafts
Performance: maximum speed 30.5kt on gas turbines; range 12,000km (7,455 miles) at 15kt on diesels
Complement: 26+174 with a maximum of 245 possible when 35 midshipmen are carried
Ships: one (Nigeria), *Aradu*

172   *The Aradu, commissioned in 1981*

Niels Juel class

Type: anti-ship guided missile patrol frigate
Country of origin: Denmark
Displacement: 1,320 tons full load
Dimensions: length 84m (275.5ft); beam 10.3m (33.8ft); draught 3.1m (10.2ft)
Gun armament: one 76mm (3in) OTO Melara L/62 DP and four 20mm (0.79in) Oerlikon AA
Missile armament: eight RGM-84 Harpoon anti-ship missiles, eight RIM-7 NATO Sea Sparrow SAMs and 48 RIM-116 RAM SAMs
Anti-submarine armament: Mk 46 torpedoes and one depth-charge rack
Mines: ships have minelaying capability
Electronics: 3D, surface-search and navigation radars, fire-control system, active search and attack hull sonar, ESM system with warning element and chaff/flare launcher
Propulsion: CODOG (COmbined Diesel Or Gas turbine) arrangement, with one General Electric LM 2500 gas turbine delivering 13,720kW (18,400shp) or one MTU 20V 956 TB82 diesel delivering 3,350kW (4,495shp) to two shafts
Performance: maximum speed 30kt on gas turbine or 20kt on diesel; range 4,625km (2,875 miles) at 18kt
Complement: 18 + 80
Ships: three; *Niels Juel*, *Olfert Fischer* and *Peter Tordenskiold*

Niteroi or Vosper Thornycroft Mk 10 class

Type: guided missile destroyer
Country of origin: UK/Brazil
Displacement: 3,200 tons standard and 3,800 tons full load
Dimensions:: length 129.2m (424ft); beam 13.5m (44.2ft); draught 5.5m (18.2ft)
Gun armament: one 114mm (4.5in) L/55 DP and two 40mm (1.58in) Bofors L/70 AA
Missile armament: four MM.38 Exocet surface-to-surface missiles and Sea Cat surface-to-air missiles
Anti-submarine armament: rocket launchers, Mk 44/46 A/S torpedoes, one depth-charge rail and one launcher for 10 Ikara missiles
Aircraft: one Westland Lynx helicopter
Propulsion: CODOG (COmbined Diesel Or Gas turbine) arrangement, with four MTU diesels delivering 11,750kW (15,760shp) or two Rolls-Royce Olympus TM3B gas turbines delivering 41,760kW (56,000shp) to two shafts
Performance: maximum speed 30kt on gas turbines or 22kt on diesels; range 9,825km (6,105 miles) at 17kt on two diesels
Complement: 21 + 179
Ships: six (Brazil), *Niteroi* + five

The small number of the crew is due to a very high level of automation

Oliver Hazard Perry class

Type: guided-missile frigate
Country of origin: USA
Displacement: 4,100 tons full load
Dimensions: length 135.6m (445ft); beam 13.7m (45ft); draught 5.7m (24.5ft) to sonar dome
Gun armament: one 76mm (3in) L/62 DP OTO Melara Compact in a Mk 75 single mounting and one 20mm (0.79in) Phalanx Mk 15 close-in weapon system mounting
Missile armament: one Mk 13 single launcher for 40 RGM-84A Harpoon surface-to-surface and RIM-66 Standard-MR SAMs
Anti-submarine armament: two triple Mk 32 tube mountings for 324mm (12.75in) Mk 46 A/S torpedoes and helicopter-launched weapons
Aircraft: two Kaman SH-2F Seasprite helicopters
Propulsion: two General Electric LM 2500 gas turbines delivering 30,575kW (41,000shp) to one shaft
Performance): maximum speed 29kt; range 8,370km (5,200 miles) at 20kt
Complement: 11 + 153 and an air unit of 48
Ships: seven (1) (Australia), *Adelaide* + five; four (Spain), *Santa Maria* + three; eight (8) (Taiwan); 51 (USA), *Oliver Hazard Perry* + 50

The US Navy's largest class of small
combatants

Oslo class

Type: guided missile coastal frigate
Country of origin: Norway
Displacement: 1,450 tons standard and 1,745 tons full load
Dimensions: length 96.6m (317ft); beam 11.2m (36.7ft); draught 5.3m (17.4ft)
Gun armament: two 76mm (3in) L/50 DP, one 40mm (1.58in) Bofors L/70 AA and two 20mm (0.79in) Rheinmetall AA
Missile armament: six Penguin Mk II anti-ship missiles and 24 RIM-7 NATO Sea Sparrow SAMs
Anti-submarine armament: Mk 46 torpedoes and one Terne III six-barrel rocket launcher
Mines: provision for minelaying
Electronics: air-search, surface-search and navigation radar, fire-control system, active/passive search and attack sonar, action information system and two chaff launchers
Propulsion: two Babcock & Wilcox boilers supplying steam to one set of Ljungstrom/De Laval geared turbines delivering 14,915kW (20,000shp) to one shaft
Performance: maximum speed 25 + kt; range 8,350km (5,190 miles) at 15kt
Complement: 11 + 139
Ships: five; *Oslo, Bergen, Trondheim, Stavanger* and *Narvik*

Peder Skram class

Type: guided missile frigate
Country of origin: Denmark
Displacement: 2,030 tons standard and 2,720 tons full load
Dimensions: length 112.6m (369ft); beam 12m (39.5ft) draught 3.6m (11.8ft)
Gun armament: two 127mm (5in) L/38 DP and four 40mm (1.58in) Bofors L/60 AA
Missile armament: eight RGM-84A Harpoon surface-to-surface missiles and 16 RIM-7 Sea Sparrow surface-to-air missiles
Torpedo armament: two twin 533mm (21in) tube mountings
Anti-submarine armament: two depth-charge racks and A/S torpedoes
Electronics: air-search and surface-search radars, navigation radar, sonar and ESM system
Propulsion: CODOG (COmbined Diesel Or Gas turbine) arrangement, with two General Motors 16-567D diesels delivering 3,580kW (4,800shp) and two Pratt & Whitney PWA GG4A-3 gas turbines delivering 32,810kW (44,000shp) to two shafts
Performance: maximum speed 32.5kt on gas turbines or 16.5kt on diesels
Complement: 115
Ships: two, *Peder Skram* and *Herluf Trolle*

Highly capable anti-ship and anti-submarine frigates with a high level of automation

Van Speijk

Type: anti-submarine and anti-ship guided missile frigate
Country of origin: Netherlands
Displacement: 2,255 tons standard and 2,835 tons full load
Dimensions: length 113.4m (372ft); beam 12.5m (41ft); draught 5.5m (18ft)
Gun armament: one 76mm (3in) OTO Melara L/62 DP
Missile armament: eight RGM-84 Harpoon anti-ship missiles and 32 Sea Cat SAMs
Anti-submarine armament: Mk 46 torpedoes and helicopter-launched weapons
Aircraft: one Westland Wasp HAS.Mk 1 helicopter
Electronics: air-search, air/surface search and navigation radar, fire-control systems, optronic director, active search and attack hull sonar, ESM system with warning element and chaff launchers
Propulsion: two Babcock & Wilcox boilers supplying steam to two sets of Werkspoor/English Electric geared turbines delivering 22,370kW (30,000shp) to two shafts
Performance: maximum speed 28.5kt; range 8,350km (5,190 miles) at 12kt
Complement: 180
Ships: six (Indonesia), *Ahmed Yani* + five

The Isaac Sweers *ex-Dutch frigate, now in service with Indonesia*